Fool's Gold

The Dearne High was designated a Specialist Humanities College in September 2007. We look to continue our success into a new Advanced Learning Centre that is currently being built to open in January 2011. 'Fool's Gold' is the second book to be published by the college. The first was 'Out WAT fantasy stories.'

The Dearne High: A Specialist Humanities College

Fool's Gold

Grosvenor House
Publishing Limited

First published in 2009
By Grosvenor House Publishing Limited
Crossweys
28 - 30 High Street
Guildford
Surrey
GU1 3HY

Typeset by Grosvenor House Publishing Limited

A CIP record for this book is available from the British Library
ISBN 978-1-907211-74-4

Head Teacher's Introduction

The publication of 'Fool's Gold represents a significant landmark in our School Improvement journey. A journey predicated upon partnership and collaborative working, which seeks to place the learner at the heart of the learning process. We promote humanitarian values whilst supporting learners in developing the skills, knowledge, understanding and emotional intelligence needed to flourish as confident, articulate, self reflective learners; learners with an increased ability to problem solve, a desire to take risks, who operate as team players with a moral purpose. In essence, learners who clearly think and think clearly, who shape and assess their own learning and who are partners in the learning process.

'Fool's Gold' has and will continue to act as a catalyst to increase students' interest and enjoyment of reading and writing alongside the development of vital Personal Learning and Thinking Skills such as creative thinking, independent inquiry, self management, effective participation and team working, vital to individual and collective success in our increasingly competitive global market.

As a community we are extremely grateful for the significant support provided in the realisation of this project and very proud of the genuinely collaborative nature of the project.

Our journey continues ...

Neil Clark
Head teacher

Sponsors

We would like to thank the following companies for very kindly donating money which paid for the book's production and a generous initial print run:

HAYS

P + K Recruitment

D.J. Byers Ltd

Globe Coaches

Barnsley Office Furniture

Arena Group

Profits from the book will be donated to the main charitable organisations that worked in partnership with us towards its completion. These include 'The National Coal Mining Museum' and the 'Whitby Parochial Church Council.'

Acknowledgements and Permissions

An enormous vote of thanks is extended to G. P. Taylor, a Children's book of the year winner and a BBC Arts and Entertainment Personality of the year, who kindly agreed to become one of the main characters within 'Fool's Gold.' The Times described 'Shadowmancer,' his first bestselling novel as: *"The biggest event in children's fiction since Harry Potter."* His Dopple Ganger Chronicles – which are identified under copyright as illustrato graphic novels, were a key influence in the devising of 'Fool's Gold.' Graham worked with the college for three days in location on a fully voluntary basis, to help us devise what we now describe as a 'virtual reality graphic novel.' He also gave up further time to discuss the full plot outline. His exemplary support spurred us all on to persuade more children's writers to work with us on a voluntary basis in return for a highly purposeful educational outcome.

My personal and very heartfelt thanks go to Joan Townend. Put simply without Joan's substantial and continually sustained support this project would never have been possible. As well as following a raft of students and staffs instructions as she took hundreds of photographs for every chapter, she worked alongside me, behind the scenes at every level and virtually every moment to make it happen.

I would also wish to offer a massive thanks to Eddie Child who not only trained our students to produce the novel's graphics images, but also led by example in their production and remained a critical friend throughout.

Many thanks to all the families of the staff and students involved who sacrificed parts of many a weekend and evening, so that their relative could make a special contribution to the work of the college!

Special thanks go to Alan McKenzie, a former chief editor of 2000AD, who provided a comic expert's viewpoint on several occasions. He helped us improve the original storyline and made some useful suggestions that were acted upon between the second and third drafts.

Thanks also to Steve Bower who proof read the first full transcript to help improve consistency on a virtually voluntary basis.

Kevin Hopgood was the only contributor to work with the college from a fully contractual origin. His professional expertise was invaluable not only in producing very polished sections based upon our instructions, but also colouring Marta

Kwasniewska's artwork and helping to generate donations for the book's production in the very early stages of its design.

Thanks go to our local but nationally recognised poet Ian McMillan and his agent Adrian Mealing, for allowing us to reproduce 'Song of the Quarryman,' writing the poem/song 'Nine Pieces of Gold' especially for the book and for allowing us to feature him as a character.

Thanks go to Chris Wooding, a Nestle Smarties Silver book award winner, for writing a diary extract to fit within the overal story and agreeing to appear as a character. Chris's latest novel 'Malice' became another main influence for ours.

Thanks also go to Alison Weir, a world renowned historian and a New York Times bestselling novelist for sending us– 'Leila' – that became included as part of the storyline. Alison Weir's 'Leila' was reproduced for the purposes of this book only – with the kind permission from the author who maintains copyright.

We were delighted with the support of Robert Swindells, twice winner of the Carnegie Medal for children's literature, twice winner of the Children's book award and who was shortlisted for the Whitbread prize, who edited the two prose sections referring to him and one of his famous bestselling books. 'Room 13' was another seminal work of children's fiction which clearly influenced the devising and writing of 'Fool's Gold.'

Thanks go to Linda Newbery, a Costa Children's Book Award winner who was twice shortlisted for the Carnegie Medal for writing a diary extract for us. The quotation at the end of chapter fifteen is from *Journal of a Sad Hermaphrodite*, by Michael de Larrabeiti, published by Tallis House. Copyright The Literary Estate of Michael de Larrabeiti 2008.

Thanks go to Bali Rai, winner of the Leicester Book Award, the Calderdale Book Award, the Angus Book Award, the Stockport School's Award and who was shortlisted for the Booktrust Teenage Prize. We were delighted that he wrote the final prose section within the penultimate chapter.

A special thank you to Joe Cornish for offering us a series of his now famous Whitby photographs that featured on BBC Breakfast as recently as May 2009. These were incorporated into chapter eleven and presented in the afterword in their original form. Similar thanks go to Mark Denton whose Scarborough pictures were incorporated into chapter six and also presented in the after word in their original form. Mark had also provided photographs to accompany several of the stories within our first book – 'Out of the Shadows: An anthology of fantasy stories.'

My ecstatic personal thanks go to Malorie Blackman, who has won virtually every children's book award there ever was many times over and to Amy Fletcher of the Hilary Delamere Literacy agency for granting special license to include the depiction of Malorie at the National Coal Mining Museum. Thanks also to my daughter Hannah for introducing me to her favourite author, who is now one of mine.

Thanks to Bernard Cornwell for his incredibly kind correspondence with some of our students and for allowing his 'playful depiction' at the end of the novel. Many would say that he remains the 'living world master' of the literary historical novel and he was therefore extremely gracious as such in his support of our own attempt to draw from his genre. The image used was based upon a photo taken by Chris Clarke, who granted permission for its use within 'Fool's Gold' only via Bernard's personal assistant Cece Motz. Chris Clarke maintains copyright thereafter.

Thank you to Jim Oldfield editor of the South Yorkshire Times and Sally Burton for allowing us to include their 'real article' about our trip to the National Coal Mining Museum as part of the actual final storyline.

Thanks to Stuart Berry, Jill Clapham, Judith Dennis and Richard Saward, at the National Coal Mining Museum for helping us to structure our real day trip and granting us permission to go ahead with our ambitious plans. We intend to donate profits from the book to the National Coal Mining Museum, as part of our role as a Specialist Humanities College.

A special thank you to the Rector Canon David Smith and the Whitby Parochial Church Council for allowing us to take photographs of the 199 Steps, the outside and inside of St Mary's Church and to Margaret Clarkson and Liz Goodhall for helping to organise the wonderful lunch at the Sea Farers Centre which we really did enjoy. We intend to donate profits from the book to the Whitby Parochial Church Council, as part of our role as a Specialist Humanities College.

Thank you to Phil Dodds who bought the first ever copy of 'Out Of The Shadows,' sold many more to developers, found us a hidden coffin for 'Fool's Gold' and posed for the initial photographs for its sequel... just in case...

Last and by no means least - thanks to all the behind the scenes people at Grosvenor House Publishing who contributed to the books' production including Kim Cross, Maggie Taylor, Ruth Pullis and Jason Kosbab whose unstinting levels of patience helped make such a complex and highly collaborative book possible.

Peter Shaw
September 2009

Endorsements

"This is a sterling and complex piece of work. My heartiest congratulations go to all those involved in completing it and making such a great job of it!"

Alan McKenzie (chief editor of 2000AD, Rampage, The Official Doctor Who Magazine, Starburst and author of 'How to draw and sell comic strips' published by Titan Books)

"Once again The Dearne High has demonstrated the extraordinary potential to be gained from bringing together creative artists and writers with the imagination, enterprise and enthusiasm of their students. This second book in their journey as a Humanities Specialist school draws upon the history of Yorkshire and its people. It's a book about time, place and the hope. Many congratulations to all involved on the accomplishment of such an ambitious project."

Jacqueline Anthony and Philippa Darley (National Co-ordinators for the 180+ Specialist Humanities Colleges)

*I've never seen anything like **Fool's Gold** before. It's bursting with surprises, and on every page there's some little gem that has kept me guessing, smiling – and completely gripped.*

It's got action, twists, drama, Dracula, vampires, some ghosts, a vicar, a good dollop of history and a whole lot more.

But for me what's so special about this book isn't in the story, it's the story behind it. What I marvel at is how so many people could have worked together, each pouring their own passion into the tale, weaving their own character into everybody else's to build something... unique. A single narrative constructed from so many voices, and yet those voices work in harmony.

Most days I sit alone in my study to disappear into a world of imagination, looking into the dark corners of my mind to dig out nuggets that I can polish up into stories. It's a solitary, sometimes even lonely, process, but one that I enjoy. The point is, I do it alone. I could never conceive of bringing together so many people, with such obviously creative minds, each searching for their own flashes of inspiration, each willing to grind out the fabric of the story to serve some greater, communal plan. It's mystifying and amazing to me.

Then the more I look through the result, this delightful book, the more I realise that it's created more than a story. It's a community. Each word in the text, every line in the wonderful artwork, holds together all the more firmly everybody who was involved in turning these ideas into a book. The story binds the people into a community, just as these pages are bound together to complete the tale.

And by reading this, you become part of the community too. So dive in and have fun – you'd be a fool not to.

Joe Craig
Author of the best selling Jimmy Coates series
September 2009

Contents

PROLOGUE

Mr Clark, the head teacher, was in a good mood, although he disguised it quite well. He was very pleased with the learning in the lesson he had observed. The children proved an absolute delight to him, as usual. Better still, many hours of leadership toil in planning for improvements in attainment and a new school build had been rewarded with financial closure. The Dearne community were now guaranteed to get the modern learning space and new prospects they had deserved. Everything that day coincided with exciting, as well as challenging, opportunities for further future improvements.

"If I could have bottled everything I saw today...I would have. The children were like raw diamonds... just imagine what they will achieve in the new Advanced Learning Centre..."

"Yes, the children were excellent" replied Mr Shaw, adding a well meaning question-

"So will you turn all our children into genies?"

"They'll manage that themselves..." replied Mr Clark. "As long as we teach them to face challenges... they'll be able to grant their own wishes."

"So how do we teach them this?" asked Mr Shaw.

"Through inspiring them and adding a little magic..."

The teacher, sitting opposite, couldn't help but move on to a bold and necessary question:

"Does that mean you could grant us all a wish like a genie from a bottle?"

"What is the wish that you want fulfilled?" asked Mr Clark curiously.

The teacher thought carefully before answering. It was important to make a multitude of wishes sound like only one. He certainly wasn't going to get three.

"A significant number of students and staff would like to collaborate on writing a new book Mr Clark. It's a very ambitious idea that is sure to involve engaging students in a series of educational visits that will help develop much needed literacy skills..."

"A series of visits?" queried Mr Clark.

"Yes, to prominent places of literary, historic and geographic interest..."

Mr Clark paused, before asking further questions intended to achieve greater clarity.

'Will this 'project' also serve to further develop the Dearne Learner vision, our rights and responsibilities agendas and above all raise standards?"

Mr Shaw thought again before answering. It was more important at this next point to make a multitude of different questions sound as though they all had one definite answer...

"Yes. "

"And how will you measure its success?"

"The response of the readers, "replied Mr Shaw.

"So be it... That said there is one thing that it had better not be!"

"What's that Mr Clark?"

The head teacher paused to attain absolute clarity this time. Now it was his turn to have a mischievous, well meaning sparkle in his eye.

"Understand this Mr Shaw, if nothing else. We undertake everything for the right reasons at the Dearne in order to ensure activities of real worth that bring about the maximum success for our students. This project must not turn out to be a search for Fool's Gold! The students had better have a truly fantastic story to tell afterwards... "

Chapter One – The Hub

"*Argh locked.... Where is a teacher when you want one?*" Jessica complained while banging on the hub door. Scott stood behind her, studying the enormous photographs on the walls. He was surprised to note that a new one now included him.

"*Are you sure it's even in there?*" Scott asked.

"*Of course it's in there. I was there last lesson wasn't I?*" Scott walked past Jessica and pressed the buttons on the lock. The door swung open as Jessica tried it again.

"*Thanks,*" she said and slipped inside. Scott followed her silently letting the door click shut behind them. Jessica walked over to the computer at the far end of the room; a grey jacket was slung over a chair.

"*I knew it was here but where is my bag? I left it here with my coat.*" She searched on chairs and under desks. Scott looked at the books in the cabinets while she searched.

"*Why did you even leave it in here when the teacher sent you off?*" Scott questioned.

"*Look I don't know why I did, I just did okay.*" Jessica snapped at him.

"*Alright keep your hair on...! Do you think the teacher would have put your bag in the storeroom?*" he asked. "*It would prevent anyone from taking it?*" Jessica strode over to the light oak door without answering and opened the storeroom.

"*Who on earth are you?*" she demanded.

A small boy, his face black with dirt, sat looking terrified across the storeroom floor, holding his eyes as though he was being forced to stare at the sun.

"*I shouldn't be here...*" the boy spluttered.

"*Then what are you doing here? And how on earth did you get here without being seen?*" Jessica asked, softening her tone. The boy sniffed.

"*I was in the mines and now I'm here.*" He sniffed again.

"*There aren't any mines open around here. They've been shut down,*" Scott said thoughtfully. The boy looked at him in disbelief.

"*I'm not allowed to take anything from the mine. My master was so angry with me... last time... he killed me...literally.*"

The boy began to sob inconsolably, as if broken. Scott shook his head.

"The mines round here were all shut down," he said flatly.

The young boy was about to speak when he was racked with a horrendous cough. He put a hand to his mouth and another across his neck. His hand was soon covered in blood. Jessica reacted instantly.

"My God! Are you alright? Scott get a teacher or someone, he needs help," she said urgently.

Scott turned and dashed to the door. Jessica followed him.

"Hurry! He isn't well. Why isn't he dressed properly? I'm scared by this. You don't think he was telling the truth do you?" she questioned. Scott shook his head.

"I don't think so," he said flatly as he walked towards the exit. Jessica got some water for the boy and returned to the storeroom. She met with another shock. The storeroom was in a terrible mess, as though it had been wilfully vandalised. Its books were strewn everywhere and the boy was gone!

"Scott!" she shouted. Scott came rushing back in.

"What's up?" he demanded and stopped when he saw what had happened.

"Where? How?" he stuttered. Both of them were bewildered.

"We shouldn't say anything about this," Scott said quietly. Jessica nodded, grabbed her bag and hurried towards the door.

It was break time by now and Mr Shaw had also told Lauren and Brandon to go to the hub and get the books they were to study next lesson.

"Finally, he's letting us do Darren Shan!" Lauren grinned.

"I know, you'd think with all the times people asked him he'd have let us read it sooner," Brandon replied.

They reached the hub's ramp and saw who was coming down and their thoughts turned to hate. Priscilla Pruman - often referred to as 'the snitch.'

"Oh it's you ... you're going in the hub? Well you'd better leave it tidy I just had to clean that up for Mr Clark and Mrs Whomersley. Someone left it in such a state. If I find it like that again I'm going to say it was you." She turned and left. Lauren stuck out her tongue at her, when she wasn't looking and carried on into the hub. Brandon tried the door on the right first, but it was locked. He tried the other door and it clicked open. They entered.

"Where did he say the books were?" Lauren asked, whilst looking at the books on the wall, one of which was signed to her.

6

"They're in the store room aren't they?" Brandon replied.
Lauren shrugged and went to open it but stopped.

"What's up?" Brandon asked.

"I'm not going in there while you're here, you'll lock me in!" she retorted.
Brandon rolled his eyes and opened the door himself and stopped short shocked.

"Who are you?" he demanded of the small boy who was sat there in the middle of the floor.

"Where am I?" he asked. His eyes were wild and he was alarmingly thin.

"You're at Dearne High. What are you doing here?" Lauren asked puzzled.

"I ... I don't know ..... One minute I was in the Three Mariners ... I ... I fell through the wall, I don't think anyone heard me... I died after they carried me into a nearby bedroom and now I'm here," the boy spluttered wiping plaster dust from his hair.

"The Three Mariners?" Brandon gasped. *"That's in Scarborough. How did you get here?"* he demanded.
Lauren pulled him away.

"Didn't Jessica tell us about seeing a ghost in the store room?" she whispered so the boy wouldn't hear.

"Yeah!" Brandon agreed.

"But didn't they say that the boy was from a mine or something similar. This one says he's from Scarborough..."
They looked back at the boy but to their surprise he was gone.

"How?" Lauren stammered.

"We've got to tell the rest about this," Brandon exclaimed.
Just then the bell went exploding like the sound of a gun.

"Let's go find them," Lauren said and turned and left whilst Brandon got the books and checked the store room again. He shut the door and raced after Lauren. They left the building quickly and to their relief Bethany, Savina, Jessica and Scott were walking past it at that very moment deep in conversation.

"Hey you lot... over here," Lauren called cupping her hands around her mouth. The group turned and walked over.

"Hey! What's up?" Bethany asked.

"You will never believe what has just happened to us!" Brandon exclaimed. *"You know how you and Jessica found a ghost in the hub?"*

"I thought you weren't telling anybody about that," Scott said, sending an acid glance at Jessica. She shrugged,

"I thought it would be ok to tell them..."

"Anyway, what I was saying ... we just saw a ghost in the hub who said he was from Scarborough," Brandon bragged.

Scott turned away, *"Yeah right!"*

"No seriously we did," Lauren protested, but the group were already walking away shaking their heads.

Later that afternoon lightening crashed into the ground around the hub. Rain rattled the windows and the metalic roof and clouds darkened the previously blue sky. Savina and Bethany huddled together just behind the doors that led inside the hub. They had been staying behind until 4 o'clock to finish a piece of prose that involved themselves as characters when the storm had started. At first they had simply ignored it, and carried on with an argument they had been having, but as the thunder cracked, their disgruntled remarks came to an end.

"I wish this storm would stop some time soon, I have to get home," Savina complained.

"I don't think we can go anywhere," Bethany said sadly.

The storm was launching thunderbolts and seemed to be attacking the small building like a vicious enemy. It seemed it was affecting the hub's electrical supply, as the lights dimmed and brightened over and over again. Savina grabbed hold of Bethany's hand and looked at her in fear. Bethany met Savina's gaze, hiding her own fear badly. Suddenly, a piece of strip lighting above the girls' heads shattered and plastic rained down on them like ice. Savina screamed. She was on edge remembering what the other four had told them.

"I think this is one of those ghosts that the others were talking about," Bethany grinned, but when another bout of sparks showered down from the ceiling, her smile vanished.

As Savina's screams pierced the air, the world around them began to warp, the air bubbled, colours changed and with a flash of bright, white light, the third ghost appeared...He wasn't like the other ghosts. This ghost was better kept this time and dressed in an attractive open cuff shirt. He appeared to be about fourteen and could be called handsome. The Ghost folded his very real looking arms and leaned against the wall.

"Ha, ha, ha, how easy it is to scare you," he smirked.

'Who are you?" Bethany demanded.

"Who I am, is not important, but it will become obvious, "he replied cryptically.

"Well, since it's obvious that you are a ghost, how did you die?" Bethany demanded enthralled at the ghost's presence.

"I was wondering when you would ask that, Bethany, "he said.

"How do you know my name?" she demanded.

"I know a lot about you, all six of you, "he said. "But in answer to your question, my father was a smuggler, which led to our family's downfall. "

He disappeared, with a wave, leaving the girls clearly confused.

"What on earth was that?" Savina gasped.

"Well it wasn't an angel was it?" Bethany asked mockingly.

"Hey stop it, just because you don't believe in what I do, doesn't mean you can make fun of me, "Savina protested.

"Says who?" Bethany retorted.

"Aarrh, this isn't going to get us anywhere. Three different, but similar ghosts, have been seen now. We need to get all of the others here to help us get this straight, "Savina said.

Bethany nodded and just as the girls agreed the rain stopped as suddenly as it had started. The clouds parted and renewed sunlight shone down.

It seemed like ages had passed before the two girls managed to contact the other four and by then the sky had darkened, indicating nightfall. The plan, devised primarily by Brandon, Scott and Bethany was to go into the hub and see if the mysterious ghosts would make another entrance so they could find out why the ghosts kept appearing. It was Friday night by the time they had all agreed. Waiting until Monday wasn't an option and even Jessica (who had been reluctant to go) said Monday was too long, to wait.

After some pushing by Bethany and Brandon, they agreed to go that night, meeting up fifteen minutes before midnight outside the moonlit school.

"It's cold, "said Lauren bitterly.

"Of course it is!" grated Savina. "It's March and England!"

The group were not exactly getting on due to lack of sleep and their worries about getting caught sneaking out. However it wasn't long before they were outside the hub, dawdling out of fear.

"How are we supposed to get inside?" asked Jessica sceptically.

Bethany smirked producing a key.

"Swiped it from a technician, the rest is all coded, but I heard the security numbers over an SLT walkie-talkie the other day..."

Lauren and Jess laughed and hurriedly pushed open the door, to get out of the cold, only to find it was even colder inside. Scott and Savina were the only ones who didn't visibly shiver as Bethany opened the door to the left hand side room of the hub. A strange form of mist flowed across the floor adopting a vague claw like shape.

"I don't know about this, "muttered Scott, hovering in the background. The rest ignored him and stepped quickly into the room, avoiding the windows and bulbs in case one ghost decided to play nasty.

They didn't have to wait long in the chilly room before odd things started to happen. The mist began to swirl around their feet and the door slammed shut, as writing appeared on the walls written in something chalky and black. Brandon, being the first to realise it was written backwards, read it:

Look Behind You.

They all looked simultaneously...

"Finally you are here, I did begin to wonder if you would come, "the man said. He was tall, dressed in dark clothes and was swinging a large golden key around his longer than average index finger.

"We came back for this?" Lauren questioned, with a mock bravado accent. Her deliberate time delaying bluff quickly melted like butter when the ghost turned his gaze on her.

"I have been watching all of you carefully. You are not aware of the plentiful opportunities that you have. My sons who visited you weren't given a wonderfully easy life... So why should you be?" he demanded.

"What have your sons got to do with us? Surely they are your responsibility?" Scott questioned.

"True and I was a very poor father indeed... I had to sell my two eldest boys to mean taskmasters to pay off my debts. I owed money to a thoroughly evil employer-Mochley, through no fault of my own."

"Mochley?" questioned Jessica.

"Don't repeat that name!" said the ghost.

"Sounds like some kind of Lord Loss type..." Brandon joked.

"Can you please stop being so selfish for once and give up some time to help them? I come pleading to you...Please save my sons..." the ghost carried on. "Their souls are in peril..."

Bethany gasped as she realized what the ghost meant.

"You mean you want us to free your sons from eternal damnation?" she asked and the ghost nodded.

"To free all of their souls you will need to make a whole series of important sacrifices. You will know when you have succeeded, because I will appear to you all one last time."

"What are they then?" Jessica questioned looking puzzled. "These sacrifices, I mean?"

"A series of challenges will come to you in turn and you must all make the right choices... BUT no one else is to know of this until much later," he said with an edge of steel in his voice. "UNDERSTAND?"

Everyone nodded.

"You will all dream of my boys in your sleep this very night and the circumstances of their deaths will be made clear. Think of some way of going to all the places where my children died, starting with the eldest," explained the ghost.

"Sounds like you've planned everything down to the last detail..." commented Scott. "I like the sound of it though... It'll be different! But how will we manage it all?"

"We'll have plenty of help from adults. Mr Clark and some of the staff in the yard are talking about us writing a book and travelling to different places of interest to go in it. We could suggest the places to visit," said Bethany. "Subtly, of course!"

"They also said that some very successful writers were being brought in to help us create our own original story..." added Jessica.

"Would we really dare to suggest writing about all of this? I mean – what would happen if nobody believed us?" questioned Bethany.

"They'd market and sell it as fiction!"

"No problems there then Scott!"

"Very funny, you two!" added Lauren. She had been quiet for a long time, listening very carefully, ready to ask the leading question:

"Will this story really be ours?"

"Of course..." replied the ghost. "It will all be yours – your challenges – your

choices – your mission to complete, but you won't be entirely on your own. When the ultimate time comes, someone specially chosen will help you."
"Someone specially chosen?" echoed Brandon.
"Yes – and that special someone has already been chosen for another purpose, but not by your teachers...and not by yourselves."

The hub lights finally dimmed and flickered off. When they flashed on again, the last and most menacing of the apparitions had gone, leaving the six students to prepare for the writing of their story.

SCOTT HAD BEEN DEEP IN THOUGHT SINCE THE VISIT OF THE THREE YOUNG BOYS AND THEIR ENIGMATIC FATHER...

JESSICA WONDERED ABOUT THE DIFFERENT PLACES WHERE THE BOYS HAD DIED...

SCOTT'S DREAM LAST NIGHT ABOUT THE ELDEST SON - A MINER BOY - HAD FASCINATED HIM.

SHE ALSO DREAMT ABOUT THE MINER BOY, AS PREDICTED, BUT FOUND THE MEMORY OF IT VERY UNCOMFORTABLE.

SCOTT AND JESSICA BOTH LEARNT THAT THE MINER BOY HAD BEEN MURDERED. THEY RETOLD HIS STORY IN CARTOON FORMAT, WITH THE HELP OF A PROFESSIONAL ILLUSTRATOR. NOW THE END RESULT WAS READY TO READ AS 'ANOTHER STORY' WITHIN THEIR STORY.

IT WAS PARTICULARLY SAD TO NOTE THAT THE DEATH OF THE FATHER'S ELDEST SON ONLY CAME ABOUT THROUGH A MISUNDERSTANDING...

15

JESSICA THOUGHT THE ESSENCE OF THEIR DREAM HAD BEEN CAPTURED AND PUT ACROSS VERY EFFECTIVELY.

SCOTT STILL FELT THERE WAS MORE TO SAY ABOUT THE MINER BOY... HE WANTED REASSURANCE FROM THE OTHERS.

THESE PAGES ARE BRILL!

WE SHOULD VISIT CAPHOUSE COLLIERY TO FIND OUT MORE.

KEVIN HOPGOOD'S DRAWINGS ARE AWESOME!

THIS PROJECT IS ABSOLUTELY UNIQUE... IT HAS THE POTENTIAL TO BRING ABOUT AN ENTIRELY NEW GRAPHIC NOVEL GENRE!

AFTER MUCH DEBATE SCOTT AGREED TO SHARE THEIR WORK WITH A KEY WRITER CHOSEN BY THEIR TEACHERS TO HELP THE COLLEGE PRODUCE A CLASSIC BOOK...

ALAN McKENZIE - HAD WORKED ON FOUR CLASSIC BRITISH COMICS. HE WAS THE CHIEF EDITOR OF THE TOPSELLER '2000AD' FROM 1991-1995.

16

BRANDON AND LAUREN HAD SEEN A DIFFERENT BOY, WHO HAD ALSO DIED IN TRAGIC CIRCUMSTANCES, THEY WERE EQUALLY ENTHUSIASTIC TO SHARE THEIR TALE WITH ALAN...

BRANDON WAS A GOOD FRIEND TO EVERYONE, PARTICULARLY LAUREN.

BRANDON HAD WONDERED IF THE GHOSTS HAD BEEN COSTUME ARTISTS HIRED BY THE TEACHERS, TO FIRE THEIR IMAGINATIONS, OR TO MAKE THE BOOK MORE BELIEVABLE... BUT AFTER THE DREAMS, HE BELIEVED THE GHOSTS WERE REAL! LIKE SCOTT AND JESSICA BEFORE THEM, THEY CHOSE TO RETELL WHAT THEY HAD LEARNT THROUGH COMIC STRIP.

LAUREN WAS AMBITIOUS, BUT LESS CONFIDENT THAN THE OTHERS.

BOTH OF THEM WERE DETERMINED THAT THEIR STORY ABOUT THE SECOND SON - THE SCARBOROUGH BOY - BE INCLUDED IN THE COLLEGE'S FORTHCOMING BOOK - EVEN IF IT WASN'T EXACTLY THEIR STORY...

The Three Mariners Inn - Scarborough

(by Lauren Eggison & Brandon Noble)

CURIOSITY

WHAT'S IN THERE?

TEMPTATION

EASY TO BREAK THE PLASTER!

SHORT TERM GAIN.

WHAT A FIND !

THERE ARE TALES WITH TERRIFIC DISCOVERIES AND TALES WITH TERRIBLE TWISTS.

LONG TERM PAIN.

I CAN'T GET OUT !

THE UNFORTUNATE BEHAVIOUR LED TO THE FIRST OF MANY SACRIFICES.

AN EXTENDED DEADLINE AND A DETENTION BROUGHT THEM BACK TOGETHER. DESTINY PLAYED A MORE SIGNIFICANT PART, ALTHOUGH THEY FOUND IT HARD TO ADMIT IT, AT FIRST.

EITHER WAY - THE END RESULT - WHEN ILLUSTRATED BY KEVIN HOPGOOD - WAS AS GREAT AS THE OTHERS.

Tales of a Whitby Cabin Boy (by Savina Lubika & Bethany Pickering)

SMUGGLERS MAKE FAR MORE MONEY THAN THOSE IN AN HONEST TRADE. I'LL FIND EVEN RICHER TREASURES HIDDEN INLAND, THAN THOSE GAINED FROM TRANSPORTING COAL BY SEA.

SEA FARERS MISSION - WHITBY.

CURIOSITY

WHAT'S IN THERE?

TEMPTATION

THIS MUST BE WORTH A FORTUNE, BUT WHERE'S MY FATHER?

TIME TO REFLECT

YOUR FATHER GAVE YOU FREEDOM AND RICHES WELL ABOVE AVERAGE.

AS YOU PREFER THESE, I WILL LOCK YOU AWAY TO ENJOY THEM FOREVER!

24

CHAPTER THREE – THE SIX STUDENTS TALK

i

Jessica contacted Scott via MSN shortly after Alan McKenzie had visited the Dearne High, to test out the students' potential for producing the college's forthcoming book.

Jessica xxx says:
Hey Scott,
Those dreams sure did freak me out; I was up all the other night thinking about it and realised there has got to be something more we could do… Alan McKenzie thought the cartoons looked great…but I don't know, I can't think straight. What do you think?
Jessica xxx

Wolf Warrior says:
Hi Jess,
Same here, every time I think about that poor boy, I can't help but feel for him. You know… He had so little going for him. Maybe we could help him, but how? We can't exactly call him in on this MSN conversation, can we?

Jessica xxx says:
No – I don't use any 'ghost software' at all – not even to back up hoards of pirate materials!

Wolf Warrior says:
Very funny…Not!

Jessica xxx says:
Got any better ideas???

Wolf Warrior says:
Maybe we could go to the National Coal Mining Museum, if only we could persuade the teachers…

Jessica xxx says:
Leave it to me; I'm practically teacher's pet, apart from Priscilla Pruman of course…lol.

Wolf Warrior says:
Are you sure we'll be allowed to go?

Jessica xxx says:
Yeah, no problem! Just mention the word educational a few times and link it in with developing our understanding of rights and responsibilities and the teachers won't be able to resist organising it… :)

Wolf Warrior says:
Don't forget to mention improving literature…

Jessica xxx says:
I think you meant – improving literacy…

Wolf Warrior says:
That's what I typed!

Jessica xxx says:
Yeah!!!

Wolf Warrior says:
Anyway it will improve our understanding of literature as well. Oh and by the way…

Jessica xxx says:
What?

Wolf Warrior says:
It's very poor grammar to use three exclamation marks at once!

Jessica xxx says:
Okay 15 all for now, as long as you admit I'm always right.

Wolf Warrior says:
I hope you're right about us being able to go to the National Coal Mining Museum!

Jessica xxx says:
Of course I'm right, I'm Jessica WRIGHT… lol

Wolf Warrior says:
Ha, doesn't it make you think though, why did the ghost visit us first, not Bethany or one of the others?

Jessica xxx says:
I don't even like visiting Beth; I can't imagine anyone else would. But I do see what you mean… maybe we're special?

Wolf Warrior says:
Yeah, but I don't think that's it, there has to be something more you know?

Jessica xxx says:
Yeah, maybe we're very special…

Wolf Warrior says:
Or maybe there's more to it than just the obvious. I mean what did that old weirdo that fathered those boys mean by 'the special someone chosen for another purpose?' And how will that be kept secret from the teachers and us?

Jessica xxx says:
That's easy – we won't be told all that, until the very end stupid! We need to get the whole thing started first – we must get these trips organised. Tomorrow!

Wolf Warrior says:
I'll talk to some teachers in the morning and you talk to Mr Clark. Agreed?

Jessica xxx says:

Agreed. I expect Mr Clark will be easy to catch in the yard at break. He's already asking students lots of questions about the book. Mr Shaw asked him if we could do it last week.

Wolf Warrior says:

Typical of Mr Shaw that! I suppose he'll be claiming that it was him who thought of the idea in the first place!

Jessica xxx says:

No way! He wanted to call us the 'Coolio Gang' !!!

Wolf Warrior says:

Let him dream. We'll be called the 'Iron Pyrates...' from now on...talking of which – if we get this trip to the National Coal Mining Museum organised, it might persuade the others to organise similar trips to Scarborough and Whitby.

ii

Jessica didn't actually need to wield her full charms with the head teacher the next day. Mr Clark thought her ideas were 'everything he would like to bottle,' the minute she began talking. They both visited Mrs Townend, the school's marketing and events officer, that same morning. She began organising a visit to the National Coal Mining Museum before lunchtime. It wasn't long before Jessica was back gloating to the others about how easy it all was. She couldn't resist challenging Brandon and Lauren to arrange a similar trip to Scarborough. Brandon and Lauren similarly decided to meet on the internet highway that evening. After all, the houses where they lived, were at least 100 metres apart...

Brandon says:

Hi, what you doing? Do you really think Jessica persuaded Mr Clark to let us visit the National Coal Mining Museum on her own?

Lauren says:

I don't know, it's hard to believe...But she said that the trip to the National Coal Mining Museum's been booked before the end of the month and that's where we're going first!

Brandon says:

Well, Jess isn't the lying type. I think I believe her, because she's never lied before, and we have known her for at least a year and a half……

Lauren says:

Well, if you believe her, then I will too, but, a GHOST trail! It's all sort of Scooby Doo and Harry Potter, isn't it? Anyway, Jessica said that you get to go on a tour in a real underground mine. The lift takes you down 140 metres!

Brandon says:

No way!

Lauren says:

I don't know… Anyway we'll ask the others tomorrow, because I haven't got a clue.

Brandon says:

Don't forget you've got a detention tomorrow.

Lauren says:

It's not fair. We've worked well since the start of the year. I've only had one detention and that's because YOU decided it was funny to throw a water balloon at Priscilla Pruman, and SHE BLAMED ME!

Brandon says:

Well, it was boiling hot, and I was bored. It was only an hour detention anyway. So are we going to discuss it tomorrow with the others, or not… I suggest we persuade Mr Child to let us do some research about Scarborough. It'll fit into our ICT work and we could get him to go to Mrs Townend and she'd help us to organise a trip there as well.

Lauren says:

Scott said that's what we have to do... He's expecting Bethany and Savina to persuade everyone to visit Whitby. Anyway, Savina told me that she was going to have an MSN convo with Bethany. To see what she thought. She will probably text me in a minute.

Brandon says:
Wrong! Savina just texted me. They came up with the same basic idea we had, Mrs Townend will have her work cut out tomorrow. Savina is bragging about her French level, what did you get? Savina says that she got a 6b!

Lauren says:
I got a 5c! What did you get, or is it so bad that you are getting moved to a lower set?

Brandon says:
Shut up! I'm a 5a! Better than yours, anyway, we'll talk about tomorrow when all six of us are there. Got to go now, going to see my grandad.

Lauren says:
OK, see you tomorrow. Don't forget your English Homework! Miss Timms will kill you if you don't do it!

iii

Mr Clark was delighted that a significant number of students and teachers were, indeed, keen to collaborate on writing a new book. The three trips that the students had requested were all organised and the 'Iron Pyrates' were very quick with permission slips to ensure they were going. Mr Shaw had decided to call the book 'Fool's Gold' as a mischievously ironic response to a well meaning challenge set by Mr Clark for all those involved. Mr Clark's suggestion that the project must not become a search for fool's gold had helped motivate Mr Shaw to enlist the support of eleven, very famous, children's writers and two famous photographers as well as a raft of teachers and students. Two of these, Bethany and Savina, wanted to share some further ideas straight away. Their next plans were also secretly recorded, because they, like the others had chosen to share them across the internet highway. It was tantamount to putting their names into print.

Bethany says:

So we're now known as the 'Iron Pyrates?'

Savina says:

Yes. Better than 'Coolio Gang'!

Bethany says:

Sounds to me like we still need a bigger crew... Why don't we invite some of the local primary schools to go with us?

Savina says:

Wouldn't they be too young and too scared...I mean...what with ghosts and the like?

Bethany says:

Young kids mature quickly nowadays... Besides the more people involved in our project the more books we're likely to sell...eventually.

Savina says:

Is that all you ever think about...being a famous author?

Bethany says:

No!

Savina says:

So what else do you think about?

Bethany says:

Being an extremely good one!

Savina says:

Typical...It's a good idea to get some more children involved though. Mr Clark will be pleased to develop further links with the primaries and we'll get one over on Scott and Jessica. Imagine their faces when they have to admit that we came up with one of the main ideas!

Bethany says:

And you suggested my motivations were sad! Still I'm glad you agree with me…

Savina says:

Sounds like poor Mrs Townend has yet another job to do!

Bethany says:

You bet! Still we all know she enjoys it! I hope we get a posh coach!

53 STUDENTS AND TEACHERS TRAVELLED TO CAPHOUSE COLLIERY ALSO KNOWN AS THE YORKSHIRE MINING MUSUEM. THEY TRAVELLED IN A VERY POSH COACH INDEED- SIX HIGHLY CONSCIENTIOUS TEACHERS THOUGHT THEY HAD PLANNED EVERYTHING DOWN TO THE LAST DETAIL - SIX STUDENTS KNEW BETTER. THE 'IRON PYRATES,' AS THE STUDENTS NOW REFERRED TO THEMSELVES, WERE PROVING VERY CREATIVE IN MORE WAYS THAN ONE.

CAPHOUSE COLLIERY WAS AN INTRIGUING SEVENTEEN ACRE SITE WITH AN EXCITING ASSORTMENT OF BUILDINGS, DISPLAYS AND GALLERIES THAT REVEALED THE UNSEEN WORLD OF MINING THROUGHOUT MANY CENTURIES.

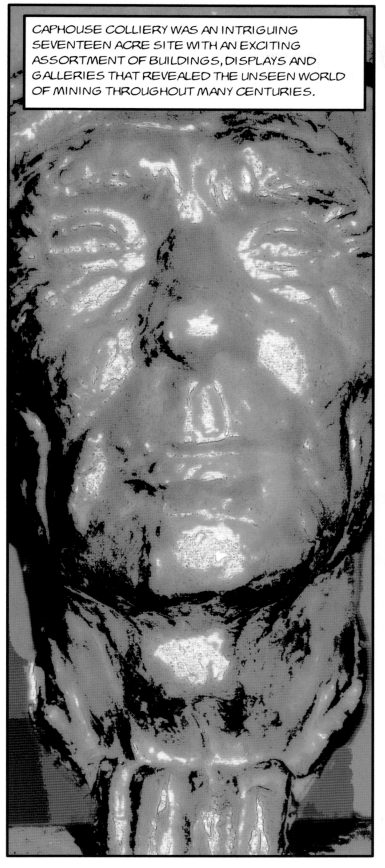

WHILE WE'RE HERE LOOK OUT FOR SEVERAL GUEST WRITERS WE INVITED. THEY'LL HELP YOU WITH IDEAS.

I WONDER WHO?

HELLO IAN, I THOUGHT WE'D SEE YOU HERE!

SONG OF THE QUARRYMAN
(By Ian McMillan)

Chorus

Sing me, sing me, sing me the deep pools of blue
Sing me, sing me, sing me the rumbling sorter

Verse 1

Sing me the hard hat
Sing me the reflection of the sun and the snow in the glasses
Beneath the hard hat

Verse 2

Sing me the rumbling sorter
Sing me the distortion of the sun and the snow in the window
Of the cabin of the rumbling sorter
And in the glasses beneath the hard hat

Chorus/Verse 3

Sing me the deep blue pools
Sing me the refraction of the sun and the snow in the surface
Of the somehow gorgeous deep blue pools
And in the window of the cabin of the rumbling sorter
And in the glasses beneath the hard hat

Chorus/Verse 4

He said 'It's an astonishing feeling'
Sun reflecting in the glasses beneath the hard hat
'To think that we're uncovering something'
Sun reflecting in the glasses beneath the hard hat
'Millions of years old'
Sun reflecting in the glasses beneath the hard hat
'And we're the first to see it'
But I couldn't hear him
For the sound of the machine's song
And the sun reflecting in the glasses beneath the hard hat

Middle Eight

Sing me the refraction
Sing me the distortion
Sing me the reflection
Sing me the uncovering
Sing me the refraction
Sing me the distortion
Sing me the reflection
Sing me the uncovering

39

AS THE STUDENTS GOT MORE AND MORE GRIPPED WITH WHAT THEY READ... THE DIFFERENCE BETWEEN REALITY AND FICTION BECAME COMPLETELY BLURRED...

TALES FROM THE MINES
By Geoffrey Carr

CHILDREN LEFT THE HOUSE BEFORE SIX EACH MORNING AND WORKED UNTIL SEVEN AT NIGHT.

THE PRIMARY STUDENTS BEGAN TO PLAN AND DESIGN THE NEXT INSTALMENT OF 'FOOL'S GOLD.'

43

DON'T TAKE THE FOOL'S GOLD. IT WILL BE THE LAST THING YOU DO.

BYE.

DO YOU THINK THAT IS TRUE?

YEAH, AND I NOW KNOW GHOSTS ARE REAL.

STORY WITHIN A STORY BY STUDENTS AT HIGHGATE PRIMARY.

FATE WAS ABOUT TO TAKE A TURN FOR THE WORSE.
UNFORTUNATELY MODERN TECHNOLOGY WAS OF NO USE....

THE PHONE YOU RANG IS SWITCHED OFF

THE PHONE YOU RANG IS SWITCHED OFF

THE TRIP UNDERGROUND HAD STRICT 'HEALTH AND SAFETY' REGULATIONS.

NO MOBILES, WATCHES, OR CAMERAS.

THERE'S GHOSTS DOWN THEM THERE MINES...

DON'T LISTEN TO HIM, YOU'LL BE FINE AS LONG AS YOU STICK WITH US.

CAPHOUSE COLLIERY IS PROBABLY THE OLDEST MINE STILL IN USE EVERYDAY IN BRITAIN. BY THE END OF DECEMBER 2000, THE MUSEUM HAD WELCOMED OVER 896,000 VISITORS.

AS THE DEARNE STUDENTS TRAVELLED 140 METRES UNDERGROUND THEY WERE ABOUT TO GAIN A GENUINE INSIGHT INTO JUST HOW HARD THE MINERS WORKED, THE MACHINERY THEY USED AND ALL ABOUT OLD MINING METHODS THAT COULD HAVE BEEN MADE EASIER BY THE TECHNOLOGY WE HAVE NOWADAYS.

IT WASN'T UNTIL THE STUDENTS HAD GONE DOWN THE MINE AND MET THE GHOST OF THE ELDEST SON - A MINER BOY BY TRADE FOR A 'VERY SHORT WHILE' - THAT THEY LEARNT TO UNDERSTAND THE CRAMPED CONDITIONS FAMILIES ONCE WORKED HARD IN... TO GAIN SO LITTLE MONEY.

THE PARTY WERE ASKED TO STAY TOGETHER AT ALL TIMES. IF ANY ONE WENT MISSING THE WHOLE PARTY HAD TO WAIT UNTIL THEY WERE FOUND.

51

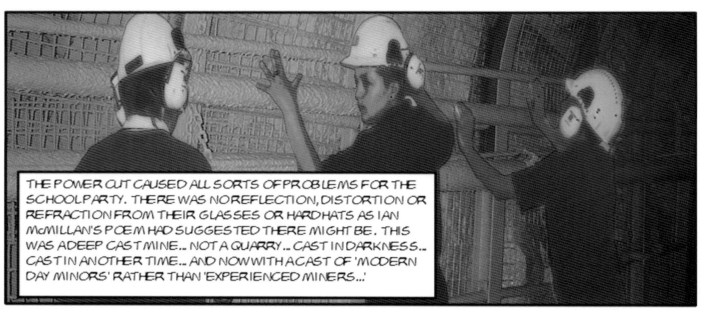

THE POWER CUT CAUSED ALL SORTS OF PROBLEMS FOR THE SCHOOL PARTY. THERE WAS NO REFLECTION, DISTORTION OR REFRACTION FROM THEIR GLASSES OR HARD HATS AS IAN McMILLAN'S POEM HAD SUGGESTED THERE MIGHT BE. THIS WAS A DEEP CAST MINE... NOT A QUARRY... CAST IN DARKNESS... CAST IN ANOTHER TIME... AND NOW WITH A CAST OF 'MODERN DAY MINORS' RATHER THAN 'EXPERIENCED MINERS...'

THERE WOULD BE PLENTY OF 'REFLECTION' AND 'UNCOVERING' HOWEVER.... AND THE STORY UNFOLDING WOULD INSPIRE ANOTHER, EVEN BETTER, SONG...

INTERESTING THE POWER IS STILL ON IN THE CONFERENCE ROOM. THE 'IRON PYRATES' MUST BE WITH A LEADING LIGHT INDEED. I'LL CONCENTRATE ON THE STUDENTS BELOW GROUND NOW.

THE GHOST BOY BEGAN MIMICKING THE VOICES OF THE GUIDES. HE MANAGED TO FOOL TWO YOUNG GIRLS WHO LEFT THE PATH ONLY SLIGHTLY BEFORE THEY WERE LOST.

THE GIRLS STUMBLED AND FELL. THEY REACHED FOR THE MINE WALLS IN AN ATTEMPT TO FIND THEIR WAY BACK. A GHOSTLY CHILL FILLED THE AIR.

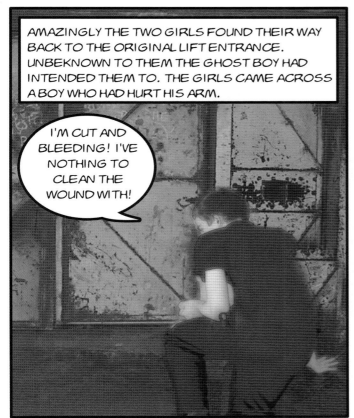

AMAZINGLY THE TWO GIRLS FOUND THEIR WAY BACK TO THE ORIGINAL LIFT ENTRANCE. UNBEKNOWN TO THEM THE GHOST BOY HAD INTENDED THEM TO. THE GIRLS CAME ACROSS A BOY WHO HAD HURT HIS ARM.

I'M CUT AND BLEEDING! I'VE NOTHING TO CLEAN THE WOUND WITH!

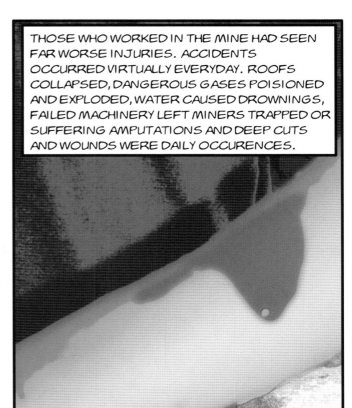

THOSE WHO WORKED IN THE MINE HAD SEEN FAR WORSE INJURIES. ACCIDENTS OCCURRED VIRTUALLY EVERYDAY. ROOFS COLLAPSED, DANGEROUS GASES POISIONED AND EXPLODED, WATER CAUSED DROWNINGS, FAILED MACHINERY LEFT MINERS TRAPPED OR SUFFERING AMPUTATIONS AND DEEP CUTS AND WOUNDS WERE DAILY OCCURENCES.

A BOY WITH A BLEEDING ARM... AND YOU WITH A SPRAINED WRIST... BOTH OF YOU ARE INJURED..!

AS THE ELDEST OF THE GHOST BOYS APPEARED HE WAS ALREADY VERY ANNOYED, THOUGH NOT SURPRISED WITH THEIR SELF PITY.

YOU CALL THAT AN INJURY... YOU HAVE NO IDEA!

ARE YOU A GHOST?

53

I WILL MAKE YOU UNDERSTAND WHAT REAL INJURIES LOOKED AND FELT LIKE. I WAS STRANGLED TO NEAR DEATH DOWN HERE.. AND DIED SHORTLY AFTERWARDS!
ALL I DID WAS PICK UP A PIECE OF ROCK THAT I THOUGHT WAS GOLD. IT LOOKED SO REAL, BUT I WAS A FOOL TO HOLD IT SO CLOSE TO MY MASTER....

YOU'RE SENDING ME THOUGHT MESSAGES!

THE GHOST BOY CONTINUED TO EXPLAIN THAT HE WAS ASKING ALL OF THE IRON PYRATES FOR HELP, BUT HE WASN'T ASKING NICELY. HE BELIEVED THAT THEY ALL NEEDED TO KNOW WHAT IT FELT LIKE TO BE PUNISHED PERMANENTLY FOR A SMALL ERROR OF YOUTH, IN ORDER TO LEARN EMPATHY.

ONCE YOU CARE ABOUT OUR PLIGHT, YOU'LL WANT TO CHANGE IT.

ALL OF YOU WILL HAVE DREAMS THAT WILL SHOW YOU HOW MUCH MORE YOUNG CHILDREN SUFFERED OF OLD, THAN YOU DO TODAY.

YOU WILL BE ABLE TO HELP US WHEN YOU HAVE FOUND THE TREASURE!

54

LET'S SEE HOW YOUR FRIENDS RESPOND TO WHAT IT WAS REALLY LIKE DOWN HERE! THESE 'HALLUCINATIONS' WILL BE SO CONVINCING THEY'LL THINK IT IS ACTUALLY HAPPENING NOW!

ALL THOSE DOWN THE MINE AT THAT MOMENT WERE SUBSEQUENTLY HAUNTED BY NIGHTMARES. THESE WERE BROUGHT ABOUT BY THE ELDEST GHOST BOY WHO WAS STANDING EXACTLY WHERE HE HAD BEEN MURDERED.

THE GIRL WAS SENT STRANGE VISIONS OF PIRATE TREASURE..

THE BOY WAS NEVER MEANT TO BE DOWN THE MINE. IF HIS FATHER HAD NOT SOLD HIM TO PAY OFF DEBTS.. HE WOULD HAVE BEEN BROUGHT UP IN WHITBY, WITH A DIFFERENT LIFE..

WHY IS HE REVEALING A VISION OF A TREASURE CHEST? HE SAID THE GOLD HE FOUND WAS FOOL'S GOLD, NOT REAL GOLD?

THE NEXT VISIONS SENT WERE FAR MORE HORRIBLE... AND NOT ONES ANYONE WANTED TO PONDER ABOUT...

ANOTHER VISION THAT FOLLOWED WAS FAR MORE FRIGHTENING. ONE UNFORTUNATE BOY WAS SUBJECTED TO A VERY GRAPHIC VISION OF THE GHOST BOY'S MURDER. HE FOUND IT IMPOSSIBLE TO EVEN BLINK, LET ALONE CLOSE HIS EYES!

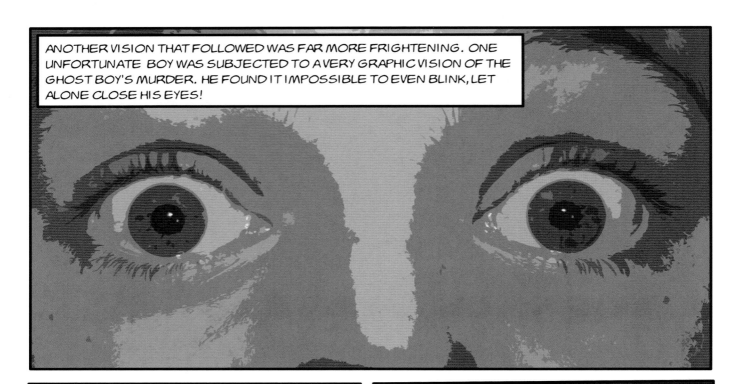

A FURTHER BOY TRIED TO CALL OUT TO THE PRIMARY CHILDREN THAT IT WAS ALL JUST IMAGINARY, BUT THE NEXT HALLUCINATIONS WERE SO DEAFENING HE COULDN'T EVEN OPEN HIS MOUTH TO SHOUT ABOVE THEM.

ONE LUCKY CHILD MANAGED TO COVER HIS EARS, BUT IT DIDN'T PREVENT THE MESSAGES SOUNDING VERY CLEARLY INSIDE HIS HEAD.

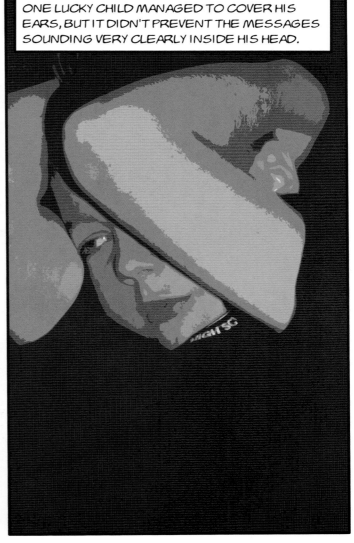

THE YOUNGER CHILDREN WERE TREATED EQUALLY WITH THE ELDEST... EQUALLY BADLY THAT IS...

WHAT IS HAPPENING TO ME?

IT MUST HAVE BEEN AWFUL!

I CAN'T BELIEVE THEY WOULD SEND SMALL CHILDREN LIKE US IN WET SACKS WITH A CANDLE TO EXPLODE METHANE...

ALL OF THE CHILDREN SAW HOW DIFFERENT THEIR EXPERIENCES WERE COMPARED TO THOSE OF YORKSHIRE CHILDREN LIVING IN THE LATE NINETEENTH CENTURY.

THE GHOST HE WAS NO OLDER THAN ME!

SOMEBODY STOP THESE NIGHTMARES... THEY'RE AGONY!

ALL OF THE CHILDREN SAW THE FULL EXTENT OF THE CRUELTY OF HUMAN NATURE.

TWO OLDER BOYS THOUGHT THEY SAW THE GHOST FOR REAL AND CALLED OUT TO THEIR TEACHER...

An Hallucination Down the Mine.

STORY WITHIN A STORY BY STUDENTS AT HIGHGATE PRIMARY.

STRANGE THAT THE ADULTS AND TEACHERS DIDN'T INTERVENE... THEY REMAINED COMPLETELY UNAWARE OF EVERYTHING. EVEN STRANGER STILL NONE OF THE SIX 'IRON PYRATES' WERE INVOLVED IN FACING THE GHOSTS EITHER.... AT LEAST NOT DIRECTLY...

THERE WERE GHOSTS OF THE PAST AND GHOSTS OF THE PRESENT ON THEIR MINDS. BUT THEY WERE DISTRACTED FOR A MOMENT BY MR SHAW'S ANNOUNCEMENT OF A VERY SPECIAL GUEST WHO HAD AGREED TO HELP THEM TURN FOOL'S GOLD INTO REAL GOLD... IAN MCMILLAN WASN'T THE ONLY LEADING LITERARY LIGHT TO ENTERTAIN AND GUIDE THE STUDENTS THAT DAY.

HE WAS NOBLE AND BRAVE, BUT HE SEARCHED FOR FOOL'S GOLD. I WONDER IF WE ARE?

THE CHILDREN WERE ABOUT TO MEET A WELL DESERVING BENEFACTOR OF THE NINETIES LITERARY GOLD RUSH...

WHO'S GOING TO HELP US?

THE ANSWER CAME QUICKLY.

THE STUDENTS WERE MESMORISED BY A MEETING WITH MALORIE BLACKMAN. THEY WERE MASSIVE FANS OF HER BOOKS AND DELIGHTED WITH HER SUGGESTIONS ABOUT GRIPPING PLOTS AND POWERFUL THEMES

I WISH I COULD WRITE LIKE HER

THIS IS MORE LIKE SEARCHING FOR REAL GOLD NOW...

INTERESTINGLY THEY WERE ALL ABOUT TO EXPLORE THE POWERFUL THEMES OF PREJUDICE, THE OPPRESSORS AND THE OPPRESSED FOR REAL... THEY WERE, AFTER ALL TRULY WITHIN THE STORIES THAT THEY HAD DREAMED OF.

YOUNG PEOPLE ARE BEGINNING TO REALISE PREJUDICE AND DISCRIMINATION BRING US TOGETHER. HOW CAN WE MOVE FORWARD IF ALL WE HAVE IN OUR HEARTS IS ANGER, VIOLENCE, HATRED AND WAR?

SINCE YOUNG PEOPLE HAVE BEEN TAUGHT TO READ AND DEVELOP SKILLS FOR LEARNING WE CAN NOW UNCOVER THE TRUTH OF WHAT HORRIBLE THINGS HAPPEN IN THE WORLD AND BUILD A BETTER ONE THAT LEARNS FROM PREVIOUS GENERATIONS' MISTAKES RATHER THAN PERPETUATING THE SAME ONES.

WE MUST NOT PRE-JUDGE PEOPLE WITHOUT GETTING TO KNOW THEM FIRST. IT IS NO LONGER ACCEPTABLE TO JUDGE BY RACE, COLOUR, AGE, GENDER, LANGUAGE, RELIGION, POLITICS OR OTHER OPINION, NATIONAL OR SOCIAL ORIGIN, PROPERTY, BIRTH, OR SOCIAL STATUS. JUST THINK HOW YOU WOULD FEEL IF YOU WERE BEING JUDGED BY ANY OF THESE THINGS. ALL YOU YOUNG PEOPLE, NEED TO REMEMBER HOW AWFUL DISCRIMINATION CAN MAKE US FEEL. YOU MUST WORK TO ENSURE DISCRIMINATION IS TOTALLY WIPED OUT EVERYWHERE.

WELL SAID! ABOUT TIME

AS POWER WAS RESTORED THE ANXIOUS STUDENTS SUDDENLY SMILED. EVERYTHING MADE SENSE. A LITERARY LIGHT HAD SHONE FORTH. THE TORMENTING GHOSTS HAD DISAPPEARED WITH THE DARKNESS.

A POWER CUT BELOW GROUND AND THREATS OF HARM WERE ONE THING, BUT NO ONE TO THEIR KNOWLEDGE HAD BEEN HARMED. IN ACTUAL FACT, SEVERAL STUDENTS FELT A RENEWED SENSE OF CREATIVE POWER. WHATEVER HAD HAPPENED, THEY WERE A STEP NEARER TO DISCOVERING THE TRUTH.

Trouble down t' pit as lights go out on Dearne's history kids

By Sally Burton

MORE than 50 Dearne school children made history themselves—on a recent research visit to the National Coal Mining Museum.

The primary and secondary age kids had to pool their skills to overcome a sudden emergency, after an unexpected power cut at the site. A core research group in the museum library were faced with no way of contacting their fellow pupils, who were deep down the pit as all power and communication was cut off.

The 53-strong pupil party from Dearne High School, Gooseacre, Dearne Highgate, Hill Primary and Dearne Carrfield schools, did manage to get reunited – and returned home newly-inspired for yet another chapter of their unique novel.

'Fools' Gold' features the haunting adventures of pupils as characters in the book, as they trail to the seaside towns of the East Yorkshire coast then inland again.

It follows the success of 'Out

Clockwise from front are: Nicole Smith, 15, Jordan Ratcliffe, 15, Abby Randerson, 15, Photographer Joe Cornish, Scott Boardman, 15 and Nicole Andrews, 14.

of the Shadows', an anthology of short stories they launched last year to high acclaim. Fools' Gold, with its "stories within stories" is even more ambitious, and enters new writing territory altogether.

It includes input from a raft of prolific children's writers. G P Taylor has worked closely with the kids around his home territory of Scarborough and Whitby. Other recognised authors, historians and screen writers involved in the venture include Chris Wooding, Darren Shan, Alison Weir, Anthony Horowitz, Robert Swindells, Bali Rai, Malorie Blackman, the Dearne's own Ian Mcmillan and Marvel comic writer/designers Kevin Hop-

good and Alan Mckenzie. Dearne High's Director of Specialism Peter Shaw said he hopes the finished product will be highly marketable. "It's an incredibly ambitious idea but it's a tremendous amount of fun, and we have a core of kids emerging here with real commitment. "We're linking education with community, business, tourism, the list is endless. And we're indebted to all the people who have lent support and encouragement. We're very excited by the whole project."
This week, landscape photographer Joe Cornish dropped by for a day at Dearne High, and he too was more than happy to help furnish the pages of the burgeoning book.

The 'Iron Pyrates' had decided to stop communicating in pairs. After their first trip to the National Coal Mining Museum, Wolf Warrior (Scott) decided they had a lot to talk about that night. The six 'Iron Pyrates' were on line at once.

Wolf Warrior says:
I can't understand why the miner ghost boy chose to threaten our friends as he did? He barely involved us in anything afterwards... I thought it was meant to be our story?

Jessica xxx says:
Sometimes you've got to give others a chance. That way you might become their leader.

Wolf Warrior says:
Okay – so what happened to our challenges, our choices and our mission then?

Lauren says:
Good question! Was it you who chose the photograph of yourself and your Y10 buddies, who didn't even go on the trip – to be in the paper?

Brandon says:
Yeah good point Lauren! I didn't realise it was your entire 'mission' Scott! I thought this story belonged to the 'Iron Pyrates?'

Jessica xxx says:
It's a fair question Scott. I thought you were all up for the 'Iron Pyrates?' So why did you choose the 'Coolio Gang' of GCSE photographers instead?

Bethany says:
He didn't. Mrs Townend wrote it all up! She thought it was wonderful meeting Joe Cornish, being a photographer herself that is. Anyway...This is all very interesting not... We should be

discussing what we learnt recently and what we're going to do next.

Savina says:
Like what?

Bethany says:
Scott might have had his photo in the paper and the school got very good publicity, but he's right. We weren't as involved as we'd have liked to be. I think that was like a lesson for us... Like I said, you can't always write your life story exactly as you want it... I think that's why so many writers decide to write fiction.

Savina says:
Cue famous writer build up - It was when Bethany Pickering finally gave up the ghost after it chose to scare other children, not her, that she knew she would be a very famous and what was it now... a 'very good' writer.

Bethany says:
Very funny, Savina!

Wolf Warrior says:
We haven't time for your 'dissent' Savina! Don't forget what Malorie Blackman said to us in the conference room at the National Coal Mining Museum. Don't prejudge people before getting to know them properly first. Please continue Bethany.

Bethany says:
I think that the ghost of the miner boy put across some real important points about the differences between then and now. He got a lot of young children to empathise with him, even though he felt he had to frighten them to do so.

Brandon says:
Yes - but why did he have to frighten them?

Bethany says:

So that when the time comes to face greater, perhaps even 'real challenges,' they'll have sort of been trained to deal with them!

Wolf Warrior says:

That was really well put Bethany!

Bethany says:

Thanks Scott! The ghost did leave several clues with the students down the mine, didn't he? Those self same students also had the common sense to share the ghost's clues with us… The miner boy ghost knew that they would. After all, the students knew that they would never have been part of this, if we hadn't asked them to join in the first place.

Jessica xxx says:

Get to the point Bethany!

Bethany says:

We now know for absolutely definite that the treasure is to be found in Whitby! The first two sons died, we know that from the dreams we had, but we never got to find out what happened to the third son, only that he was locked in some sort of treasure store. We have to find that treasure store and then we will be able to save their souls! The ghost of the miner boy made clear to the girl that the treasure still remains hidden. It's there for the taking, but we mustn't take the 'Fool's Gold.'

Wolf Warrior says:

How will we know the difference?

Bethany says:

What do you mean?

Wolf Warrior says:

How will we know the difference between 'Fool's Gold' and the 'real gold?'

Brandon says:
One of us might be above a 3c in Geography!?

Wolf Warrior says:
I was referring to the truth! How will we get to the truth?

Jessica xxx says:
Yes – Isn't that what the ghosts said in the library Scott? It's our mission to 'uncover' the truth.

Bethany says:
Oh yes, Jessica – here we go again – 'calling in all the local papers…' 'calling Scott…' 'calling our leader,' 'calling mission control,' 'calling lover boy'…oh sorry, isn't that the same thing…?

Savina says:
Lay off Bethany!

Wolf Warrior says:
What do think we should do then Bethany?

Bethany says:
I think we should go straight to Whitby, it's obviously the most important place, find the treasure, save the souls of the boys and have done with it!

Brandon says:
That's not fair Bethany! We haven't been on our trip yet! What about Scarborough?

Wolf Warrior says:
You're very quiet Lauren? Are you still on line?

Lauren says:
Yes!

Wolf Warrior says:
So what do you think?

Lauren says:
It was supposed to be our story – our challenges, our choices, our mission. Something tells me it's only when we've learnt to overcome very difficult challenges and made a number of difficult choices, including those laid out for us in Scarborough, that we'll be able to complete our mission in Whitby.

Wolf Warrior says:
I agree…absolutely.

Bethany says:
So do I! After all, missing out on Scarborough would also mean having to spend an extra day in school. Besides, we'll probably have to gather plenty more clues in Scarborough, before we know what to do in Whitby…

Savina says:
Yes, and don't forget we'll have to find the specially chosen one...

Wolf Warrior says:
Good point. I'd nearly forgotten about him or her… I wonder if we'll find out in Scarborough? What will the old sea side resort have in store for us…other than fish and chips…

Jessica xxx says:
More places to visit…more writers to meet…and probably some more clues about the circumstances of the ghosts on the way!

CHAPTER SIX - A VISIT TO SCARBOROUGH

THE SCHOOL PARTY WOULD COVER MOST OF THE TOWN BETWEEN THEM THAT DAY.

THEY WERE TO MEET G.P.TAYLOR AT THE GRAND HOTEL AND THEN EXPLORE IN SMALL GROUPS.

OTHER KEY DESTINATIONS INCLUDED THE THREE MARINERS INN, ANNE BRONTE'S GRAVE, SCARBOROUGH LIBRARY, AND THE GOLDEN GRID.

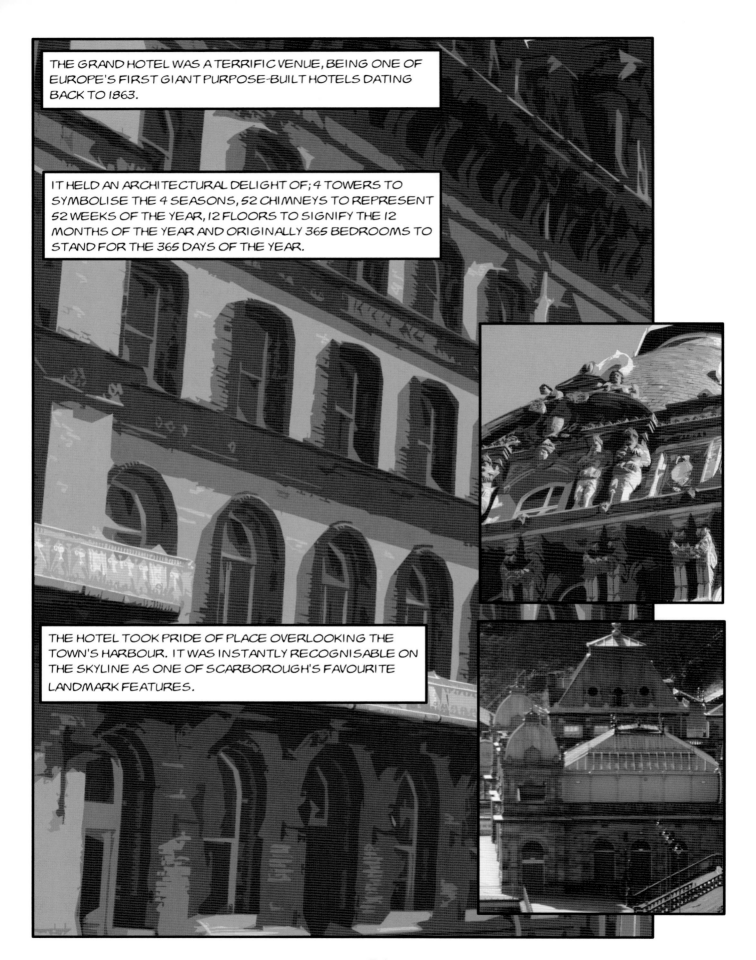

THE GRAND HOTEL WAS A TERRIFIC VENUE, BEING ONE OF EUROPE'S FIRST GIANT PURPOSE-BUILT HOTELS DATING BACK TO 1863.

IT HELD AN ARCHITECTURAL DELIGHT OF; 4 TOWERS TO SYMBOLISE THE 4 SEASONS, 52 CHIMNEYS TO REPRESENT 52 WEEKS OF THE YEAR, 12 FLOORS TO SIGNIFY THE 12 MONTHS OF THE YEAR AND ORIGINALLY 365 BEDROOMS TO STAND FOR THE 365 DAYS OF THE YEAR.

THE HOTEL TOOK PRIDE OF PLACE OVERLOOKING THE TOWN'S HARBOUR. IT WAS INSTANTLY RECOGNISABLE ON THE SKYLINE AS ONE OF SCARBOROUGH'S FAVOURITE LANDMARK FEATURES.

THE UPSTAIRS BALLROOM, INSIDE THE GRAND HOTEL, WAS THE IDEAL SETTING TO MEET UP WITH...

THE REVEREND...

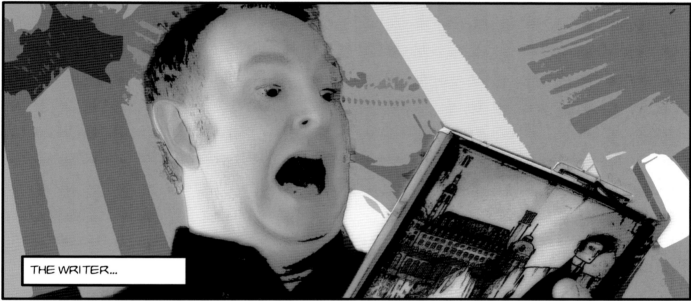

THE WRITER...

THE PERFORMER.. AND ABOVE ALL...

THE CHILDREN'S FRIEND, G.P. TAYLOR, KNOWN SIMPLY TO DEARNE STUDENTS AS 'GRAHAM.'

GRAHAM HAD WORKED WITH THE COLLEGE FOR A FULL DAY TO HELP WITH THE PRODUCTION OF THEIR FIRST BOOK - 'OUT OF THE SHADOWS - AN ANTHOLOGY OF FANTASY STORIES,' IN NOVEMBER 2007. SHORTLY AFTERWARDS HE UNDERTOOK A JOINT SIGNING WITH DEARNE HIGH STUDENTS AND THEIR LOCAL PRIMARY PARTNER SCHOOLS AT W H SMITHS.

GRAHAM HAD VERY KINDLY OFFERED TO ASSIST THE DEARNE HIGH AND ITS PRIMARY PARTNER SCHOOLS WITH THEIR FORTHCOMING NOVEL - 'FOOL'S GOLD' - IT HAD BEEN INSPIRED BY HIS ILLUSTRATO NOVELS - 'THE DOPPLE GANGER CHRONICLES.'

NO ONE COULD HAVE KNOWN JUST HOW MUCH HE WAS GOING TO HELP THEM AND IN HOW MANY WAYS...

MANY OF THE STUDENTS WERE DELIGHTED TO SIMPLY HAVE THEIR PHOTO TAKEN WITH GRAHAM, OTHERS ENJOYED HIM SIGNING THEIR BOOKS, WHILST THE 'IRON PYRATES' HUGGED UP DEVIOUSLY CLOSE - HOPING TO ASK IF HE KNEW ANYTHING ABOUT GHOSTS...

AS SOON AS ALL THE PHOTOGRAPHS HAD BEEN TAKEN, A MASS OF STUDENTS LINED UP EAGERLY TO HAVE THEIR COPIES OF 'DOPPLE GANGER' AND THE 'MARIAH MUNDI' SERIES SIGNED. GRAHAM ALSO GAVE OUT FREE 'MARIAH MUNDI' BOOKMARKS, BADGES AND PLAYING CARDS. THE 'IRON PYRATES DIDN'T GET THEIR CHANCE TO ASK HIM ABOUT GHOSTS. GRAHAM WAS VERY CAREFUL TO GIVE EACH STUDENT EQUAL AMOUNTS OF HIS TIME...

SHORTLY AFTERWARDS, HE TOOK THE STUDENTS AROUND THE NOW FAMOUS MARIAH MUNDI TRAIL.

IT'S IMPORTANT WE STAY TOGETHER AT THIS POINT. WE WILL BE DIVIDING YOU INTO SMALLER GROUPS SHORTLY.

GRAHAM TAYLOR'S TOUR TOOK THE SCHOOL PARTY THROUGH NARROW STREETS, THE TOWN CENTRE AND DOWN TO THE LESSER KNOWN PARTS OF THE OLD TOWN. THE DAY WAS TO BE A VERY EXTENSIVE 'LITERARY AND HISTORIC EXPLORATION' INDEED!

SHORTLY AFTERWARDS, THE MAIN GROUP SPLIT INTO FOUR. SCOTT, JESSICA AND SEVERAL OTHERS REMAINED WITH GRAHAM.
MR CHILD'S GROUP HEADED TOWARDS THE THREE MARINERS INN TO SHARE RESEARCH FINDINGS WITH CHRIS WOODING.

MISS THOMPSON'S GROUP WENT TO VISIT ANNE BRONTE'S GRAVE. MR SHAW AND 'THE ICT TEAM' WENT TO MEET AND WORK WITH ALISON WEIR AT SCARBOROUGH LIBRARY.

NARROW STREETS AND DARK ALLEYWAYS CAST FAMILIAR SHADOWS. ALL OF THE VENUES PROVIDED DISCRETE HIDING PLACES FOR THE GHOSTS OF THE THREE BROTHERS, NOT TO MENTION OTHER GHOSTS SOON TO BE DISCOVERED...

THE GHOSTS VISITED THE CHILDREN AGAIN AND AGAIN, AS THOUGH FOLLOWING THEM. IT WAS, HOWEVER, THE CHILDREN FOLLOWING THE GHOSTS.... OR TO BE MORE PRECISE - FOLLOWING THE GHOSTS' INSTRUCTIONS..

EXCERPT FROM CHRIS WOODING'S DIARY
(by Chris Wooding)

Got a call from a Mr Child today. Teacher from a college somewhere up north. Seems he phoned the Three Mariners Inn in Scarborough, asking about a dead boy. I guess the staff told him I'd been there recently, asking the same kind of questions, and they put him on to me. I just thought the stories about the inn were a bit of historical colour. Fun stuff to put in my next book. I thought that what I saw there was just a trick of the light.

But now I wonder...

Child told me about how students have been seeing ghosts in his college. How they've started having nightmares, reliving the experiences of those ghosts. So far, so crazy; but one of their stories rang a bell with me. The story of a kid who went exploring in the old inn, who fell through some plaster and got trapped in a locked storeroom. Poor little sod hammered on the door, but nobody heard him. Nobody missed him. Nobody came.

He died in the bedroom next to the storeroom. Whatever they were storing there, it clearly wasn't food.

Child's proposing to take a bunch of students to investigate the inn. Wants me to take them along. I wonder if that's a good idea. They should probably just shut that place up and throw away the key.

But I'm going anyway. I have to know if what I saw in that storeroom was just my imagination.

Because what if it *wasn't?*

THE AREA TO EXPLORE AT THE THREE MARINERS INN WAS QUITE SMALL, SO THE PARTY DECIDED TO SPLIT IN HALF.

THE VISITS PROVIDED SEVERAL WINDOWS OF OPPORTUNITY... AND AN ILLUMINATING AND SMASHING TIME WAS HAD BY ALL...

JACK, CAITLIN, CALLUM AND EMILY OF THE HILL PRIMARY DECIDED TO EXPLORE THE FRONT OF THE BUILDING FIRST. THEIR SUBSEQUENT STORY WAS INCREDIBLE, BUT BRANDON AND LAUREN REFUSED TO BELIEVE IT - EVEN WHEN IT WAS VERY CONVINCINGLY ILLUSTRATED BY KEVIN HOPGOOD.

Three Mariners Inn

SOMETHING APPEARED IN THE WINDOW...

WHO'S THAT IN THE WINDOW? IT'S...

CRASH!

IT'S A GHOST!

HEY, YOU'RE NOT SCARY.

I WAS A CHILD LIKE YOU!

JACK RAN TO TELL THE CHILDREN AND FELL.

HA! HA! HA! HA!

CAITLIN, CALLUM AND EMILY WERE ALL STILL SCARED AND WANTED THE GHOST TO LEAVE.

PRECISELY WHOSE STORY IT WAS, WAS PERHAPS FAR MORE COMPLICATED THAN CHRIS WOODING, OR ANYONE ELSE INVOLVED FOR THAT MATTER, EVER IMAGINED. THE GHOSTS OF THREE BROTHERS HAD MORE IDEA THAN MOST AS TO WHAT WAS MEANT TO HAPPEN. THEY WERE THEREFORE VERY RELIEVED THAT THINGS WERE GOING TO PLAN.

NEITHER MR CHILD OR MR WOODING HAVE INTERFERED WITH ANYTHING. BRANDON HAS DISCOVERED THE GUN POWDER AND RESISTED THE TEMPTATION TO USE IT AT THE WRONG TIME.

MR SHAW REMAINS IN THE LIBRARY AS INTENDED. HE'S THINKING ABOUT JACK'S MESSAGE AND BETHANY AND SAVINA WILL SOON PROVIDE EVERYONE WITH FURTHER 'MOTIVATIONS' FROM THE GRAVEYARD.

MR TAYLOR IS PLAYING HIS PART WELL TODAY, BUT IT IS VITAL THAT EVENTS OCCUR IN SUCH A WAY AS TO ENSURE HE REMAINS WITH THE CHILDREN ALWAYS, UNTIL EVERYTHING IS RESOLVED.

THERE WERE PLENTY MORE CLUES TO GATHER ALONG THE MARIAH MUNDI TRAIL THAT DAY. INTERESTINGLY, NONE OF THEM HAD ANYTHING WHATSOEVER TO DO WITH THE MASTER STORYTELLERS 'MARIAH MUNDI' SERIES... PERHAPS GRAHAM HAD BEEN PLANNING SOMETHING ELSE ALL ALONG!

I CAN CERTAINLY FEEL THEIR PRESENCE AND ALMOST SEE THEM. THEY'RE TRYING TO TELL US SOMETHING.

BETHANY WAS INSPIRED TO ASK MISS THOMPSON EVERYTHING THERE WAS TO KNOW ABOUT THE LIVES OF THE BRONTES.

SHE WASN'T ENTIRELY SURE HOW SHE WOULD FIT THEIR FINDINGS INTO THE SCHOOL'S BOOK AND MORE IMPORTANTLY SHE WONDERED IF THERE WAS A LINK BETWEEN THE BRONTE GHOSTS AND THOSE OF THE THREE YOUNG BOYS. IT WAS A REAL SHAME THAT THESE APPARITIONS DIDN'T TALK.

SO YOU'RE RIGHT! OTHER GHOSTS EXIST..

SAVINA WAS GRADUALLY BECOMING MORE CONVINCED ABOUT THE RELEVANCE OF THE VISIT... YOU COULD SAY - SHE WAS 'ENTERING INTO THE SPIRIT' OF THE OCCASION, OR AT LEAST THAT 'HER SPIRITS WERE IMPROVING.'

SHE WAS PARTICULARLY INTERESTED IN HEARING HOW TINY THE BRONTE'S WRITING WAS IN ORDER TO FIT ON THE VERY LIMITED AMOUNTS OF PAPER THEY COULD AFFORD.

MISS THOMPSON SAID IT DIDN'T MATTER ABOUT THE BRONTE'S BEING DEAD - THEY WERE STILL ABLE TO COMMUNICATE TO ANYONE THROUGH THEIR LITERATURE. SHE READ ANNE BRONTE'S POEM - 'VANITAS VANITATUM, OMNIA VANITAS.'

UPON HEARING THE POEM AND STUDYING THE GRAVE - BETHANY REALISED THERE WAS ANOTHER LINK BETWEEN ANNE BRONTE AND THE THREE YOUNG BOYS... ANNE'S LIFE WAS ALSO TRAGICALLY CUT SHORT. SHE DIED AT THE AGE OF JUST 28.

"AND ERE ONE GENERATION DIES, ANOTHER IN ITS PLACE SHALL RISE; THAT, SINKING SOON INTO THE GRAVE, OTHERS SUCCEED, LIKE WAVE ON WAVE..."

THE LAST AND BY NO MEANS LEAST IMPORTANT GROUP HAD GONE TO VISIT SCARBOROUGH LIBRARY TO MEET UP WITH ANOTHER BEST SELLING AUTHOR CALLED - ALISON WEIR.

SUMMER, KENNEDY, NATALIE, ASHLEY AND SEAN, MADE UP THE 'ICT PRODUCTION TEAM.' IT WAS TO BE THEIR ROLE TO SET OUT THE GRAPHIC PAGES FOR THE COLLEGE'S FORTHCOMING BOOK. THEY WERE EXPECTED TO RESEARCH AND GATHER CONVINCING 'BACKGROUND DETAILS' WITH REGARD TO SCARBOROUGH AND WHITBY.

'LEILA' (by Alison Weir)

Martin was shocked to see Leila in the corner seat by the bar. Shocked to the core. It was, after all, three months since he had lost her, and he was not a man who believed in the supernatural. He could not get the memories of that terrible train crash out of his head.

But no, it was Leila to the life. Blue jeans, embroidered top, spiky chestnut hair and oh-so-sexy red lips. He had loved kissing those lips.

He caught his breath. Was she an illusion, conjured up by his grieving, needy brain? How could this be? Death had brought to a tragic end their brief time together, and the dead can never come back.

Yet evidently – if he could believe the proof before his own eyes – they could. It was definitely her sitting there in their favourite seat, and she was looking about her as if she were expecting to see someone. Then their eyes met, and locked together. Hers were irradiated with emotion. Amazement, love, delight and, yes, fear – he could read them all in her startled, glistening eyes and parted lips. Of course she would be fearful: she would realise the effect her being here must have on him. He might run, be frightened away – many people would – and she would lose him forever. But he was not the running sort – and he had loved Leila deeply.

Had the other drinkers noticed her there? He glanced about him. No one seemed aware of anything unusual. And that wasn't surprising really, since Leila looked so...substantial, so normal, sitting there looking lovingly and incredulously at him. And of course, if she had had to choose a place to return to him, it would have been here, where they had spent most of their happy evenings.

Courage, man, he said to himself, as he walked towards her, expecting her to disappear at any moment. He wondered what it would feel like to touch her. Would he feel the wonderful physicality of her once more? Or would his hand pass straight through her?

"*Leila?*" he whispered, looking down at that lovely face with its sensual, cherry-red lips.

"*Martin? Is it really you?*" Her eyes, he saw, were brimming with tears.

"*How can this be?*" he asked her. "I thought... I mean, I know what happened." Carefully, now, he told himself. She might be in denial. He had heard of spirits who didn't realise that they had passed on and had to be gently helped to wherever it was that they were destined to go. He remembered that film with Patrick Swayze...

She did not answer, but just continued to stare at him, tears trickling down her cheeks.

"*Are you all right, love?*" a man sitting nearby enquired concernedly.

"*I'm okay,*" she answered, still looking longingly at Martin.

"*It's alright, she's with me,*" Martin said quickly. The man turned away, duty done.

Martin sat down next to Leila. Strange, he was touching her arm, but he could feel nothing. She was insubstantial then; appearances were deceptive. He swallowed his disappointment. At least he could see her, could feast his eyes upon her.

"*Leila,*" he said again, his voice a whisper. "*Leila, you came back to me. How?*"

Then suddenly the tears welled and he sat beside her weeping his heart out, right there, in the middle of the Cricketers' Arms. And no one took any notice of him. Typically British, he thought, struggling to control himself. Turn your heads away, that's right! Even the man who had spoken to Leila ignored him.

Leila was staring at him intently.

"*Can you hear me?*" he asked her quietly, and attempted a smile.

She did not respond. He felt faint, disorientated. This couldn't be happening. Only minutes ago, he'd been... Where had he been? He couldn't recall. His vision was blinded, his memory blanked, by the sight of Leila. Those vivid green eyes, eyes he'd never thought to see again, eyes that had closed for ever in death – or so he had thought.

He noticed a scar on her cheek – a scar he'd never seen before. Probably an injury she'd received in the crash, he supposed. Did the dead still bear their injuries in the hereafter? It didn't make sense. Surely she had suffered mortal wounds? The scar was evidence of a wound that had healed. It wasn't logical. But then seeing her here wasn't logical either.

"Darling," he said, almost entreating her. "Leila, say something to me, please."

But she was looking beyond him. He turned and saw his friend Mike entering the pub. Mike, whom he hadn't seen for some time now. When was the last time they had played squash together? It would be good to have a drink and catch up.

"Leila." Mike walked past him, bent down and greeted her with a kiss on those cherry-red lips, then sat down.

"Are you okay?" he asked, looking at her anxiously. "You look as if you've seen a ghost!"

"I think I have," said Leila.

102

CHAPTER TEN - EVERYONE MEETS BACK TOGETHER AT THE GOLDEN GRID

THE DEARNE PARTY OF 53 MET BACK TOGETHER AT THE GOLDEN GRID - A SPACIOUS THREE-FLOOR RESTAURANT THAT SERVED THE VERY BEST IN SEAFOOD DISHES, AS WELL AS THE FINEST FISH AND CHIPS ON SANDSIDE.

IT WAS VOTED THE BEST RESTAURANT 2007 IN THE YORKSHIRE COAST TOURISM OSCARS AND DESCRIBED AS THE "BEST FISH AND CHIPS IN THE WORLD" BY THE GUARDIAN IN 2006. THE STUDENTS COULDN'T WAIT!

THE WHOLE OF THE SECOND FLOOR OF THE RESTAURANT HAD BEEN RESERVED ESPECIALLY FOR THEM...

THE TABLES WITH THE VIEW OF THE HARBOUR WERE KEPT SPECIFICALLY FOR GRAHAM TAYLOR AND DEARNE STAFF.

BETHANY PONDERED ON WHY THE GHOSTS KEPT PASSING ON MESSAGES TO THE 'IRON PYRATES' THROUGH OTHER STUDENTS...

THE ADULT GHOST WHO APPEARED LAST OF ALL IN THE HUB MENTIONED MAKING SACRIFICES TO SAVE THE SOULS OF HIS THREE SONS... WE'VE GATHERED LOTS OF CLUES ... BUT WE'VE ONLY ONE TRIP LEFT IN WHICH TO DO IT.....

EVERYONE THOROUGHLY ENJOYED
LOOKING AT THE 'MARIAH MUNDI'
MEMORABILIA. THE LARGE SERVINGS
OF FISH AND CHIPS WERE OF A RARE
QUALITY AND QUICKLY CONSUMED!

STUDENTS FROM THE DEARNE, THE HILL, GOOSEACRE AND HIGHGATE, POSED WITH GRAHAM FOR THE SCARBOROUGH EVENING NEWS.

IT WAS TO BE THE FIRST OF MANY SUCH SCHOOL VISITS TO THE NOW FAMOUS 'GOLDEN GRID.'

CHECK INSIDE THE HUB WHEN YOU ALL GET BACK TO COLLEGE. I'VE LEFT SOME VERY IMPORTANT CLUES ON ONE OF THE POSTERS.

MRS TOWNEND GOT TO MEET THE REAL 'CAPTAIN JACK' AS WELL AS THE FAMOUS AUTHOR...

I'M INTRIGUED!

WHEN THE 'IRON PYRATES' RETURNED TO THE COLLEGE, THEY WENT STRAIGHT TO THE HUB WITH MRS TOWNEND AND MR SHAW TO CHECK OUT WHAT GRAHAM MEANT.

HE HAD TOLD THE STUDENTS TO REMEMBER THE FIRST THINGS THAT HE HAD EVER TAUGHT THEM.

AT FIRST THEY WERE VERY PUZZLED...

MRS TOWNEND HOWEVER HAD NOT FORGOTTEN THE IMPORTANCE OF GRAHAM'S NOTEBOOK, WHERE HE RECORDED HIS FIRST IDEAS FOR HIS BOOKS.

WHEN EVERYONE LOOKED AT GRAHAM'S NOTEBOOK MORE CLOSELY, THEY WERE ASTONISHED. THEY HAD ALWAYS THOUGHT IT CONTAINED THE FIRST IDEAS FOR MARIAH MUNDI.... BUT NOW SOME DIFFERENT WRITING HAD APPEARED...

the magical objects
of Fool's Gold
Brandy
Gunpowder
Key
Poem

HAD GRAHAM KNOWN WHAT WAS GOING TO HAPPEN ALL ALONG? WHY MENTION THE OBJECTS AFTER HE HAD GONE? THE ANSWERS CAME THICK AND FAST WHEN THE CHILDREN REALISED WHAT WAS IN THEIR BAGS.

SCOTT FOUND A BRANDY BOTTLE THAT GRAHAM HAD SAID MIGHT COME IN HANDY ON ANOTHER OCCASION... BUT HOW? (UNBEKNOWN TO THE 'IRON PYRATES' THE BOTTLE WAS ACTUALLY FILLED WITH TEA...)

BRANDON FOUND THE GUNPOWDER KEG THAT HE HAD LEFT BEHIND AT THE THREE MARINERS INN. WHY?

LAUREN FOUND A RUSTY OLD KEY INSIDE HER HOLDALL. WHERE HAD IT COME FROM AND WHAT WAS IT FOR?

BETHANY AND SAVINA FOUND A COPY OF THE ANNE BRONTE POEM THAT HAD MYSTERIOUSLY APPEARED IN A PHOTOFRAME.

ALL FOUR OBJECTS WERE TO FIND THEIR WAY TO WHITBY... THE STUDENTS AND MR SHAW WOULD TAKE THEM EVEN THOUGH THEY DIDN'T YET UNDERSTAND THEIR SIGNIFICANCE... THEY WOULD ALL PLAY A PART IN FREEING THE SOULS OF THE GHOSTS.

As soon as they'd all returned home, the 'Iron Pyrates' were back on the internet highway to discuss the day's events and plan for their final trip to Whitby.

Brandon says:
Well it was worth going to Scarborough after all wasn't it?

Bethany says:
I suppose so. Mr Shaw certainly thought that he'd learnt something very deep and meaningful from Alison Weir's 'Leila' story. I think it was the first time that he actually began to believe our stories about the ghosts might have some truth to them.

Brandon says:
Yeah... but I'm still slightly annoyed with him.

Bethany says:
You're annoyed with HIM?

Brandon says:
Yes.

Lauren says:
I think it's because he was blamed for the broken window at The Three Mariners Inn. Mr Shaw might be more inclined to believe in ghosts than he was, but he suspects that Brandon put Jack up to texting him to say it was a ghost. Mr Shaw thinks it was probably Brandon.

Brandon says:
And it wasn't! I was completely innocent!

Lauren says:
Yes - innocently dropping hidden gunpowder barrels from the downstairs windows!

Brandon says:

I wasn't going to use them! At least not yet. I reckon I'll get to soon though. Graham would never have given us those objects unless he meant us to use them.

Wolf Warrior says:

Don't get too carried away. He might be making it all up, for a bit of fun.

Bethany says:

You're wrong Scott. He's your favourite author for goodness sake. Haven't you worked it out yet? Surely he's the specially chosen one, or whatever it was the ghost said before he disappeared?

Wolf Warrior says:

I'm beginning to think that we dreamt all of that up Bethany. Why haven't the ghosts spoken to us since?

Bethany says:

Well the Bronte's kept me very busy and they really enjoyed Miss Thompson reading them one of Anne's poems.

Lauren says:

Oh not that again… Like we're really supposed to believe that you met the ghosts of the Brontes!

Savina says:

And why ever not! It's not as though we haven't met ghosts before.

Lauren says:

Yes – but the Brontes were famous! What would they want with you?

Bethany says:

The same as all the other ghosts we've met. They wanted to be remembered and respected…

Wolf Warrior says:

This is all getting a bit heavy… I think I'll switch off shortly. I can't imagine what I'll do with a bottle of brandy while I'm in Whitby.

Jessica xxx says:

I can. And you'll bring it with you - full!

Wolf Warrior says:

Okay - It'll be difficult keeping it hidden from the teachers though.

Brandon says:

A lot easier than a barrel of gun powder though, eh Scott? Still, I can't wait to use it. I've been looking up all about it on the internet.

Wolf Warrior says:

You should watch yourself doing that. You can get arrested for less nowadays!

Savina says:

I'm surprised that you're still allowed to go to Whitby.

Lauren says:

He's only allowed because Mr Shaw says he'll hold me responsible if anything like it happens again. Brandon will be on his best behaviour, rest assured!

Brandon says:

You sound like my mother!

Jessica xxx says:

Calm down you two! Let's all remember we had a great day and we've another even better one in store! Don't forget the fish and chips. It was fantastic! Who ever heard of a school party being bought fish and chips gratis… The teachers must be very confident that we're writing a classic!

Wolf Warrior says:
Like I said, I think I'll be switching off now. Something tells me I'll need the rest. Tally ho… See you all soon! Who knows – We might even get to meet Dracula in a few days time.

Jessica xxx says:
Remind me to get his autograph!

THEY'RE COMING TO THE RESCUE... WITHIN THE HEARTLAND OF OUR FATHER'S WORST ENEMY..

WHITBY TOWN'S LITERARY AND HISTORIC TRADITION IS AS IMPORTANT TODAY AS EVER... THE NEXT CHAPTERS IN ITS NOW FAMOUS LITERARY EVOLUTION ARE ABOUT TO TAKE PLACE TODAY. A WHOLE SERIES OF 'LITERARY GIANTS' HAVE PRODUCED TIMELESS CLASSICS ABOUT WHITBY AS THE WORDS FROM ONE OF ST MARY'S GRAVEYARDS ECHO WITHIN ANOTHER -
"AND ERE ONE GENERATION DIES,
ANOTHER IN ITS PLACE SHALL RISE;
THAT, SINKING SOON INTO THE GRAVE,
OTHERS SUCCEED, LIKE WAVE ON WAVE..."

ONE PARTICULAR SCHOOL PARTY IN MARCH 2009, WERE TO COME ACROSS A LIVING LITERARY GIANT ALMOST IMMEDIATELY...AND QUITE BY ACCIDENT...

"*Doesn't get much better than this,*" Bob Swindells told himself, as he sat on the harbour wall at Whitby, gazing up at the clear blue sky of a perfect March day. He inhaled deeply, relaxing as the tangy air filled his lungs. Behind him, a supermarket seethed with activity as locals and trippers came and went, collecting and carrying away their various needs and wants. Robert smiled to himself, conjuring a scene inside somebody's shopping bag involving a purple alien by the name of Aubergine and a squad of native spuds who were hunting him. Crazy notion, but when you're a writer of fiction it pays to be a little bit crazy.

Bob loved Whitby, with its Captain Cook statue, its whalebone arch and its proud history of fishing, whaling and exploration. The town had inspired the immortal Bram Stoker, and a hundred years later it had inspired Bob in a smaller way, causing him to write one of his best known books, 'Room 13.'

He was thinking about 'Room 13' when a commotion broke out behind him. A coach had drawn up, disgorging a gaggle of students who headed straight for the public lavatories. By an amazing coincidence, some of them were actually talking about his book. It was the sort of moment that gladdens a writer's heart, and Bob got out his diary to record it before it slipped away.

Whitby harbour is a beautiful place, even on a chilly morning such as this. As I was taking my usual stroll down to the quay, I came upon a school party disembarking from their coach. As they piled out of the vehicle, I could hear them talking excitedly about various aspects of the town, and was both astonished and gratified to hear someone mention 'Room 13,' saying how much it had scared her. I passed by, leaving them to gaze up at the abbey, silhouetted against the morning sky. Perhaps, I thought, these youngsters will produce a sequel to my book, to be called something like, ROOM 14 - The Return of the Dead.

It was a happy thought, but it was driven from my mind by something new that was grabbing the students' attention. A man had appeared, and began talking to them about something called 'Shadowmancer.' I recognised a fellow author, G.P. Taylor, whose book of that title was set in Whitby.

I was turning away when a quiet voice said, "Robert Swindells?"
I turned and saw a shortish man whose complexion was so youthful he might have been one of the students. I nodded.

"Yes, I'm Bob Swindells," I told him. I spoke quietly, conscious of Taylor's presence nearby: it was his moment and I was anxious not to seem to be getting in on the act, so to speak.

"What can I do for you?"
The man hesitated.

"I ... wondered if I might have your autograph?" he said. My name's Mr Shaw. Our school is writing a book entitled 'Fool's Gold', which will be set in Whitby. We're here to research our book, and we'd love it if you'd sign our copy of yours."
He pulled out a battered copy of 'Room 13.' I signed the title page and added this message: Best of luck to the authors of Fool's Gold – sell a million. Mr Shaw looked at what I'd put.

"When our book's successful," he said, "we'll thank you for supporting us," he said. "We'll refer to 'Room 13' in part three of our book: we didn't feel we could write about Whitby's literary tradition and not at least mention it."

AFTER MR SHAW HAD MET ROBERT SWINDELLS, THE SCHOOL PARTY WALKED TO THE HARBOUR.

WHITBY TALES ARE AS TALL AS THE VERY HIGHEST AND GRANDEST OF THE TOWN'S SAILING MASTS. THEY ARE POLISHED AND PRESERVED WITH GREAT CARE LIKE THE MOST VALUABLE OF SHIPS.

IT IS A SHAME THAT SHIPS AND THEIR STORIES ARE OFTEN SOLD FOR SINGLE OWNERSHIP. WE WERE FORTUNATE INDEED, THAT THE NEXT CHAPTERS' VIEWS, TALES AND TREASURES WERE TO REMAIN WITH US ALL, FOR EVER...

WHEN THE WINDS ARE DOWN, THE SAILS ARE UP. THERE'LL NOT BE WAVES TODAY... PERHAPS WE'LL HAVE TO MAKE OUR OWN LATER!

THE SUN SHONE WITH A GOLDEN HUE THAT DAY. THE SKIES AND WATERS WERE CLEAR AND THE WINDS GENTLE. EVERYWHERE WAS AS TRANQUIL AND CALM AS A WELL TAKEN PHOTOGRAPH.

IT WAS THE PERFECT DAY FOR LISTENING TO STORIES OUTSIDE. THE STUDENTS RELISHED TALKING TO AND QUESTIONING GRAHAM TAYLOR. NO ONE SUSPECTED A THING. ONLY MR SHAW KNEW THAT THE REVEREND, WAS ALSO A TRAINED EXORCIST...

THE SCHOOL PARTY WERE DESTINED TO CROSS THE BRIDGE INTO THE OLD TOWN...

A PLACE OF NARROW STREETS, WITH FREQUENT REMINDERS OF SAILORS AND THEIR HOMEGROWN SMUGGLERS' TRADE. IT WAS THE PERFECT PLACE TO FIND SUNSHINE AND FRESH AIR. THE YOUNG WRITERS WERE SOON INSPIRED TO PRODUCE INNOVATIVE RE-TELLINGS OF CLASSIC YORKSHIRE TALES...

THOSE WHO CONTINUALLY SEEK SUCCESS ONLY FIND 'FOOL'S GOLD.' HOWEVER THOSE WHO ENJOY AND DESERVE SUCCESS, FIND ' REAL GOLD!'

SOON, WE'LL WALK THROUGH THE ARCHWAY THAT BEGAN ALL GHOST STORIES. IT IS THE MOST HAUNTED AND EVIL PART OF WHITBY... BE CAREFUL!

THE FIRST GHOST STORIES GRAHAM TOLD, STOOD ASIDE FROM THE REST...THEY CONTAINED REAL HISTORICAL FACTS THAT INSPIRED THE WORST OF ALL WHITBY'S TRUE AND IMAGINARY HORROR STORIES...

THIS PLACE HAS A DARK AND EVIL CHILL...MANY OF THE OLD SMUGGLERS WERE CRUEL TYPES AND A SERIOUS THREAT TO CHILDREN!

WATCH THE ROOFTOPS AT ALL TIMES. I FEAR WE ARE BEING WATCHED!

ANOTHER THEORY ABOUT WEARING SHADES IS THAT THEY SIMPLY LOOK "COOL." ONCE AGAIN THIS DEPENDS ON WHICH WAY YOU VIEW THEM FROM. SHADES HELP HIDE WHAT THE VIEWER IS LOOKING AT BECAUSE THEY REFLECT BACK ANYONE LOOKING AT THEM. SHADES ALSO LEND A SENSE OF POWER TO THE WEARER.

EITHER WAY, THEY DO NOT INTEREST A MOCHLEY VAMPIRE. AFTER ALL MOCHLEYS HIDE IN THE SHADE UNTIL NIGHTFALL. THEIR 'COOL' IS SEEING IN PITCH BLACKNESS AND HAVING THE POWER TO SENSE WHO SEARCHES FOR THEM!

"ONCE UPON A TIME THE MOCHLEYS BUILT AND RULED MOST OF THE TOWN, BECAUSE THEY OWNED THE LAND TO START WITH. THEY WERE GOOD AT KEEPING WHAT THEY OWNED AND TOOK EVEN MORE TO PREVENT LOSING WHAT THEY HAD.

THE MOCHLEYS ONCE MADE SEVERAL MEN CARRY DEMARCATION STONES TWO MILES TOWARDS SCARBOROUGH TO REARRANGE BOUNDARIES. THE MEN MANAGED IT. THE MOCHLEYS WERE TWO MILES OF LAND RICHER. THE MEN WERE SEVERAL POUNDS LIGHTER OR POORER, - DEPENDING ON WHICH WAY YOU VIEW IT..."

SOME SAID THEIR GREED ENCOURAGED THEIR DESIRE FOR BLOOD, OTHERS SAID THEIR EVENTUAL DAMNATION LED THEM TO BECOME VAMPIRES...

EITHER WAY, IT IS UNLIKELY THE MOCHLEYS KEPT ANY RICHES IN THE AFTER LIFE... A GLANCE AT THE ROOFTOPS WILL PROVE THIS.

IT IS A GOOD IDEA TO WEAR SHADES WHEN SEARCHING FOR MOCHLEY VAMPIRES. THE OLDEST MEMBERS OF THEIR FAMILY NOW HIDE FROM THE LIGHT, AMONGST THE SHADOWS OF ANCIENT ROOFTOPS AND THEIR RAFTERS. LOOKING UPWARDS AT THEM, CAN CAUSE BLINDNESS IF YOU STARE AT THE SUN.

IMAGINE THE RELIEF FOR THE TEACHERS, AS STRONGER SUNLIGHT PREVENTED A VAMPIRE RISK ASSESSMENT AND PROVIDED SAFER PASSAGE TO HALLOWED GROUND. EVERYONE LISTENED TO THE OLDEST AND NEWEST OF STORIES. THESE WERE TOLD WITH A RARE CHARISMA AND SPONTANEITY...

THE MODERN DAY STORYTELLER MESMORISED ALL WITH HIS NEXT SELECTION OF LIGHTER TALES. HE WOVE WITHIN THEM THE THEMES OF WONDERLUST, THE VARIANCE OF THE WINDS, THE WICKEDNESS OF THE CHANGING WAVES AND WHITBY'S FAMOUS LITERARY CHARACTERS WHO NEVER TRULY LIVED OR DIED...

PASSERS-BY LISTENED TO 'SHADOWMANCER' YARNS, OF HOW THE YOUNG AND OLD WERE CHASED BY THE BLACK DOG...OTHERS STOOD NERVOUSLY BITING THEIR NAILS, GATHERING GLIMPSES OF GENTLEMEN PERSUED BY CUT THROATS AMIDST THE GAPS IN ALLEYWAYS...

EVERYONE MARVELLED AT GRAHAM'S ORATORY SKILL AND INCISIVE COMMENTS... ONLY THE 'IRON PYRATES' THOUGHT OF THEM AS REAL...THEY NOT ONLY BELIEVED IN GHOSTS, THEY HAD MET, AND AGREED TO ENTER INTO THEIR WORLD. NOW THEY COULD EXPECT TO ADD VAMPIRES TO THEIR LIST OF PROBLEMS, PROBLEMS THEY KNEW THEY HAD TO SORT QUICKLY!

SEVERAL MINUTES LATER THEY FACED THE FAMOUS 199 STEPS...THE SELF SAME STEPS THAT DRACULA AND THE MOCHLEY VAMPIRES WALKED...THE SELF SAME STEPS THAT MANY, MANY PEOPLE TROD ACROSS THE PASSAGE OF TIME...SO MUCH SO, THAT THE STEPS THEMSELVES NOW NEEDED SUPPORT...

THE SCHOOL HAD OBTAINED SPECIAL PERMISSION FROM THE WHITBY PAROCHIAL CHURCH COUNCIL TO WALK UP THE STEPS AND TO VISIT ST. MARY'S.

THE REVEREND GRAHAM TAYLOR HAD TRAINED AS A CURATE THERE. IT WAS A PLACE OF FOND MEMORIES. HE WAS GOING TO GIVE A TRULY UNIQUE TOUR OF THE CHURCH AND THE GRAVEYARD.

St. Mary's Church
Whitby Abbey

THE CHURCH WARDEN MET THE SCHOOL PARTY AT THE ENTRANCE TO THE CHURCH. HE WAS QUITE DETERMINED TO ENSURE THAT GRAHAM BEHAVED HIMSELF....

GRAHAM BEHAVED PERFECTLY, AS DID THE CHILDREN. IT WAS, AFTER ALL, A PERFECT DAY WEATHER WISE AND A PERFECT DAY FOR POSING FOR THE WHITBY GAZETTE AND THE GENERAL PUBLIC.

A LONE PHOTOGRAPHER TOOK A STRANGE PICTURE OF A SET OF OTHER PHOTOGRAPHERS; ONE STOOD ON A GRAVE TAKING A PICTURE OF GRAHAM AND THE CHILDREN, ONE HOLDING A CAMERA SMILING AND ANOTHER SIMPLY SMILING... VIRTUALLY EVERYONE FORGOT THEMSELVES...

CHEESE!

EVERYONE THAT IS EXCEPT BRANDON AND LAUREN. AT LEAST THEY STAYED FOCUSED ON THE MORE IMPORTANT TASK OF SEARCHING FOR CLUES AMONGST THE GRAVESTONES.

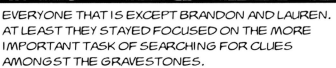

DRACULA WASN'T BURIED HERE. HIS SUPPOSED GRAVE IS ACTUALLY THAT OF A KNIGHT'S TEMPLAR! DRACULA MUST BE BURIED SOMEWHERE ELSE!

THE COLLEGE DONATED TEN COPIES OF 'OUT OF THE SHADOWS' FOR THE PRIVILEGE OF LOOKING ROUND.

DO WE HAVE TO BE QUIET?

ST MARY'S CHURCH WAS UTTERLY UNIQUE! THE PARTY LEADER TOOK NOTES FOR THE COLLEGE'S FORTHCOMING BOOK...

OF COURSE, MR SHAW AND THE STAFF HAD MORE IDEA THAN MOST AS TO WHICH DETAILS WOULD BE INCLUDED IN THE FINAL BOOK, BUT THERE WERE FORCES AT WORK WELL OUT OF ANY OF THE AUTHOR'S CONTROL THAT DAY...

THOSE WHO SAT IN THE BOX PLACED THEMSELVES ABOVE THE REVEREND'S PULPIT. THEY THEREFORE LOOKED DOWN ON THE MAN APPOINTED BY GOD!

MANY PEOPLE BELIEVE THOSE WHO SAT IN THE BOX STILL HAUNT THE WHOLE OF THE WHITBY AREA..... AS 'MALCONTENTED SOULS.'

THE REVEREND GRAHAM'S SPECIALLY PREPARED TALK, ONLY HINTED AT SOME, NOT ALL OF THE TERRORS AND CHALLENGES AHEAD!

GRAHAM CONTINUED WITH HIS REFERENCES TO WHITBY FOLKLORE OUTSIDE THE NEW VISITOR CENTRE.

MEDIEVAL THUGS TERRORISED THE LOCAL PEOPLE FOR CENTURIES. THIS LED TO MANY MYTHS AND LEGENDS ABOUT GHOSTS AND VAMPIRES.

STOKER'S DRACULA CREATED AN EXAGGERATED FEAR OF EVIL!

I'M GLAD WE BROUGHT GRAHAM!

TIME FOR DINNER... GET READY FOR LOTS OF BLOOD RED KETCHUP AT THE SEA FARERS' CENTRE...

DON'T UNDERESTIMATE HIM...

HE'S BEING DAFT!

THE PARTY RETURNED DOWN THE 199 STEPS, READY FOR A WELL EARNED LUNCH...

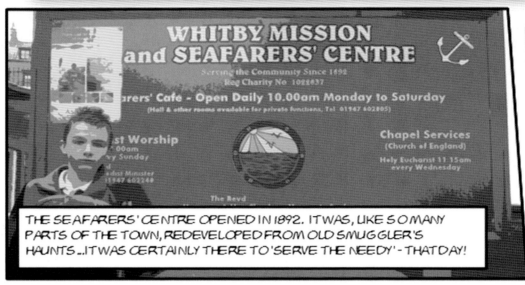

THE SEAFARERS' CENTRE OPENED IN 1892. IT WAS, LIKE SO MANY PARTS OF THE TOWN, REDEVELOPED FROM OLD SMUGGLER'S HAUNTS...IT WAS CERTAINLY THERE TO 'SERVE THE NEEDY' - THAT DAY!

MRS WILMOT PLAYED ALONG WITH THE SEA FARING TRADITION...TO DISTRACT HUNGRY STOMACHS...

AHOY ME HEARTIES! THESE BE OLD PIRATE HAUNTS...

WILL WE FIND TREASURE?

I'M STARVING!

THE SCHOOL PARTY MARVELLED AT THE ENORMOUS MURAL OF THE WHOLE TOWN ACROSS THE BACK WALL. HOWEVER, THE 'IRON PYRATES' BARELY NOTICED IT. THEY WERE NOW 'DESPERATE' TO TALK TO GRAHAM.

GRAHAM HAD COME ALONG TO SAY FAREWELL. HE WANTED TO SPEND SOME MORE TIME WITH HIS FAMILY THAT AFTERNOON. HE HAD ALREADY GIVEN A SUBSTANTIAL AMOUNT OF TIME TO THE STUDENTS AND FREELY.

NOW IT WAS TIME FOR HIM TO GO... BUT NOT WITHOUT AN OLD TRADITIONAL THANKS.

THREE CHEERS FOR GRAHAM!

HIP! HIP!

HE CAN'T BE GOING NOW! I FELT SURE HE WAS THE SPECIALLY CHOSEN ONE! HOW WILL WE COPE ON OUR OWN?

YOU WERE GREAT!

HURRAY!

GOODBYE GRAHAM!

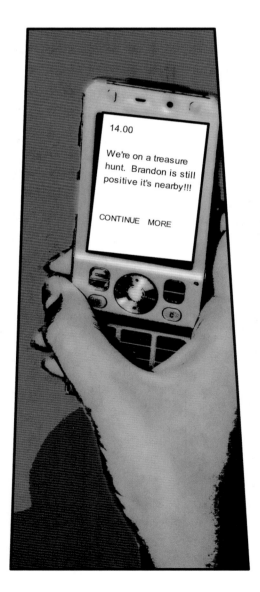

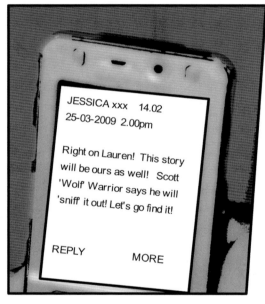

ONCE AGAIN THE GHOST OF THE THIRD AND YOUNGEST SON POINTED THE WAY FORWARD...

USE THE KEY LAUREN!

BRANDON AND LAUREN PAUSED AS THE OTHERS CAUGHT THEM UP. THEY LOOKED PAST THE HIDDEN ALLEYWAY FOR A CONCEALED ENTRANCE. THE 'IRON PYRATES' NOW FELT CERTAIN THAT THEIR MISSION WAS DRAWING TO ITS CLIMAX.

SOMETIMES EVEN THE WILDEST OF DREAMS COME TRUE. MAGIC DOES EXIST, HOWEVER SHORT IT LASTS.

NO ONE KNEW WHY LAUREN DROPPED THE KEY, AND HOW IT WAS THAT IT POINTED TOWARDS A LOCKED TRAPDOOR. A TRAPDOOR WITH A HIDDEN STAIRWAY UNDERNEATH IT, A HIDDEN STAIRWAY THAT LED TO A SECRET COVE.... THAT WAS NOW NO LONGER SECRET...

LOOK WHAT I'VE FOUND!

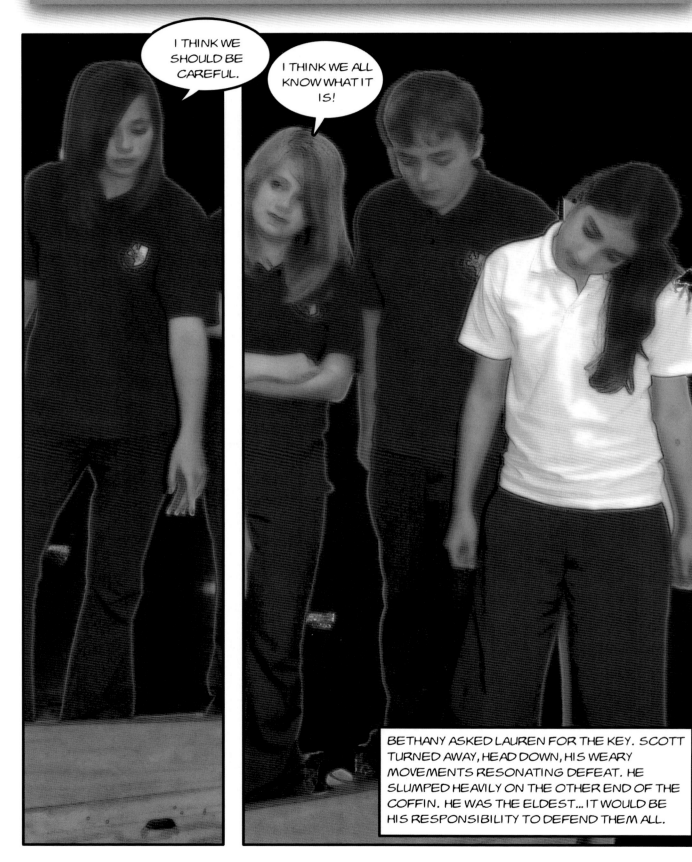

I THINK WE SHOULD BE CAREFUL.

I THINK WE ALL KNOW WHAT IT IS!

BETHANY ASKED LAUREN FOR THE KEY. SCOTT TURNED AWAY, HEAD DOWN, HIS WEARY MOVEMENTS RESONATING DEFEAT. HE SLUMPED HEAVILY ON THE OTHER END OF THE COFFIN. HE WAS THE ELDEST... IT WOULD BE HIS RESPONSIBILITY TO DEFEND THEM ALL.

The coffin groaned like a wounded buffalo. Startled, Scott backed off. Savina took his place.

"It's just a box," she told him, "it won't bite."

Scott moved in beside her, and the others gathered round, watching Bethany's efforts to twist the key she'd taken from Lauren. Absently, Jessica trickled a stream of rubies and diamonds from one hand to the other. Bethany breathed hard, jiggling the key in the lock. It was hopeless: rusted beyond use. Frustrated, she landed a violent kick on the coffin, then ground her heel into a side panel, which cracked. This brought a response from inside the casket, which juddered under the strain of a mighty blow.

The children fled screaming to a corner of the room, where they stood trembling, all eyes riveted to the booming, shaking coffin. The banging ceased, there was a moment's silence, then the coffin lid was raised from within. Mist rolled out, turning the cove into a chamber in a gothic novel.

As the children stared, petrified, a tall figure rose to a sitting position in the box. The gems fell from Jessica's hand, rattling on the floor like hail. The figure left the coffin, drifting towards the watchers like a wraith on the mist. It looked like a man, whose deathly pale face contrasted sharply with the sombre, formal jacket he wore over a blood-red waistcoat. His bowtie was black and bat-shaped, which seemed fitting, as did the long white canines he showed as he spoke.

"Why do you wake me?" he hissed, quivering with suppressed outrage. "Why do you wake Count Dracula?"

The children stared, too terrified to reply. Brandon gulped. Swindells' book was fiction .... wasn't it? Yet the ghastly apparition hovering over them was unmistakably a vampire. He screwed up his courage and stepped forward.

"We ... we didn't mean to wake you," he stammered, "it was an accident."

"SILENCE!" screeched the wraith. Brandon stood his ground but didn't speak again.

"I know your plans," grated the vampire. "Your Fool's Gold, your alliance with the man Taylor. I know everything, for I AM DRACULA and will never die: never be overthrown." He barked a short laugh.

"Did you really think Fliss and her friends had finished me? Those puny mortals, with their short lives? And you with yours – do you imagine you can conquer me?" He laughed again. "You weak, pathetic, meddling fools. YOU WILL ALL DIE TODAY!"

143

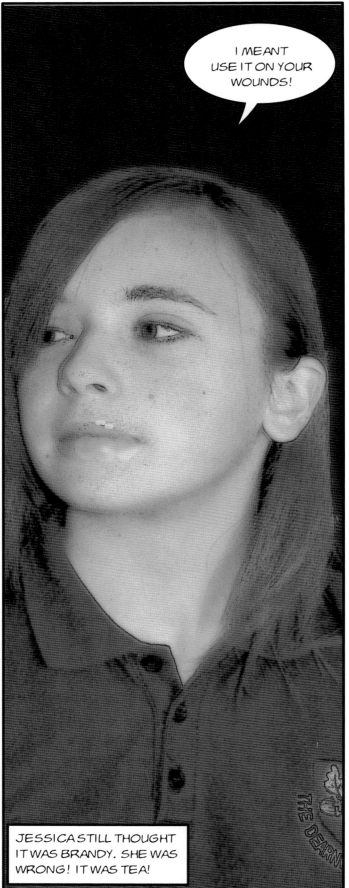

144

SCOTT GATHERED THE MOTIVATION AND NECESSARY FOCUS.

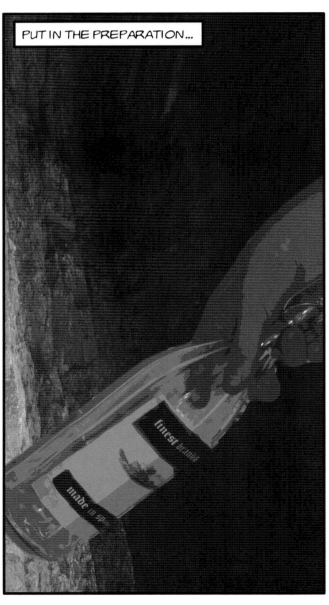

PUT IN THE PREPARATION...

GAVE HIMSELF AN EDGE...

BRANDON ADDED THE FINAL TRADITIONAL KILLING TOUCH...

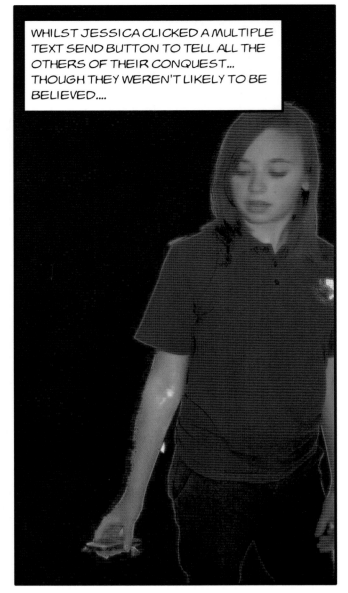

WHILST JESSICA CLICKED A MULTIPLE TEXT SEND BUTTON TO TELL ALL THE OTHERS OF THEIR CONQUEST... THOUGH THEY WEREN'T LIKELY TO BE BELIEVED....

I WILL BE BACK! HOW DARE YOU RELEGATE ME TO THE SUBPLOT OF YOUR STORY!

SCOTT AND JESSICA WERE DELIGHTED TO SEE GRAHAM AGAIN. HE GUIDED THEM THROUGH A HIDDEN DOOR INTO A ROOM THAT LOOKED LIKE A LIBRARY... THOUGH THEY MIGHT HAVE BEEN IMAGINING THAT. SCOTT WAS AGHAST AS GRAHAM TOOK OUT A CROSS FROM HIS POCKET AND MR SHAW ARRIVED.

WE'RE IN THE ROOM WHERE THE LAST BOY WAS LOCKED AWAY TO DIE AREN'T WE?

SUDDENLY GRAHAM DID SOMETHING THAT THE STUDENTS HAD NEVER WITNESSED- EXORCISM.

WILL YOU CHILDREN PROMISE TO MAKE USE OF YOUR IMPROVED OPPORTUNITIES AND REMEMBER OUR SACRIFICES?

THE GHOSTS MADE THE CHILDREN PROMISE SOMETHING.

WILL YOU USE THE SKILLS OF READING FOR YOUR FUTURE BENEFIT?

GRAHAM TOLD THE GHOSTS THAT THE CHILDREN WOULD KEEP THE PROMISE.

I'M SURE THEY WILL KEEP THEIR PROMISES.

THE GHOSTS ASKED ANOTHER FAVOUR.

WE HAVE DIED PAINFULLY AND NOT FROM OUR OWN FAULT.

CAN WE NOW FIND PEACE QUICKLY? WE DON'T WANT TO FEEL PAIN AGAIN.

154

THE GHOST OF THE THIRD BOY
FOLLOWED THE OTHERS.

MR. SHAW HANDED
GRAHAM THE KEY.

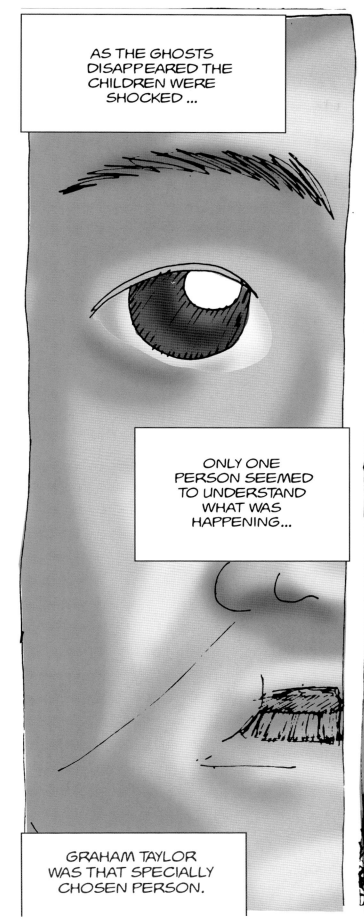

AS THE GHOSTS DISAPPEARED THE CHILDREN WERE SHOCKED ...

ONLY ONE PERSON SEEMED TO UNDERSTAND WHAT WAS HAPPENING...

GRAHAM TAYLOR WAS THAT SPECIALLY CHOSEN PERSON.

THE MOMENT HAD COME AS PROMISED AT THE BEGINNING. THE FATHER OF THE BOYS STOOD BEHIND THE LAST SON TO BE SAVED.

TODAYS YOUNG PEOPLE HAVE REALLY HELPED YOU ALL. NOW YOUR WHOLE FAMILY CAN REST IN PEACE. BE ASSURED THAT MOCHLEY WILL NOT GET AWAY WITH HIS CRIMES.

THE STUDENTS LOOKED LIKE THEY HAD BEEN RELEASED FROM AN ENORMOUS BURDEN.

IT HAD ALL HAPPENED SO SUDDENLY... BUT NOW THE STUDENTS FELT BETTER.

The staff and pupils struggled to come to terms with all that they had seen and been party to, especially Jessica: the ghosts of three young boys, their father and Dracula himself. Was it real? How could it be real? Were they in fact stumbling through a waking nightmare – a mass delusion?

Then Jessica saw it, on the dusty ground, away to the left, past resplendent rubies and glittering bars of solid gold. A skeleton! Knowing instinctively that she had discovered the earthly remains of a character unaccounted for, she told the others. Graham walked across to the find and studied it.

"Such a waste..." he whispered, as the pupils joined him in his sympathy, a few of them shaking their heads in sorrow. The skeleton lay with hands grasped outwards, as though seeking to keep hold of an enormous quantity of wealth.

Graham turned to Jessica with an instruction:

"Place this key next to the skeleton," he said.

As soon as Jessica did as she'd been asked yet another ghost began to materialise through the gloom.

"What the Devil...!" shouted Mr Shaw, as some of the pupils backed away, towards the hidden door they had found, far later than the 'Iron Pyrates.'

The apparition standing before them wore a sardonic smile, carrying an enormous padlock and key, which was pulsing and glowing in a bright, golden hue, making the treasure all around them sparkle with light.

"Mochley!" gasped Jessica.

"Indeed," replied the most intimidating ghost of all. "How good of you to remember my name."

The rest of the group recognised Mochley too. It was he who'd locked the third boy in with the treasure, knowing that the poor wretch would die there, amidst the diamonds and pearls. Surrounded by enough wealth to buy almost anything except for the one thing he'd crave – his freedom. The ghost knew their thoughts.

"Very fitting don't you think?" he asked them, his eyes fixed on Graham. "Fools' Gold indeed..."

"But why did you...?" began Jessica, seeking an answer, only for Mochley's ghost to silence her with a rasping sound.

"YOU THINK I WILL ANSWER TO YOU!" bellowed Mochley's ghost, his voice echoing around the room, making the walls vibrate and scattering golden sovereigns across the floor.

The rest of the group took yet another collective step backwards as Graham attempted to focus his mind once more, ready for one last battle. Jessica stood perfectly still, unperturbed, her trust in the exorcist/author total.

"How utterly delightful," continued the ghost, *"that I, Mochley, have been given back the key to lock you away, so that I will be triumphant for eternity whilst you will meet your end here,...such wonderful irony."*

One by one, it dawned on everyone that the ghost was right. Here they were, in the very same pit in which the third boy had met his end, about to suffer a similar fate. Well maybe not everyone. Graham lifted his head, his eyes blazing like balls of fire, as he held out the crucifix.

"Some forces are stronger than either you or I can imagine," he whispered to the ghost.

"Too late!" spat the ghost. *"I SHALL NOT BE DEFEATED!"*

But Graham refused to be cowed, his hand steady, his will like iron. An incantation left his mouth, repeating itself over and over, taking on a life of its own. The ghost began to convulse as the padlock and key it carried turned first amber then scarlet and back again. Suddenly it began to thrash about violently, screams of desperation escaping its mouth like bombs, resounding through the room and causing the treasure to scatter.

Some of the pupils screamed in terror, some turned to the trapdoor. Jessica, for her part, wondered whether Graham had taken on too much this time. His hair and clothes were drenched in sweat, his face red with exertion. She edged towards him, hoping that he would not suffer in trying to save the rest of them. But she needn't have worried. The ghost gave a final convulsion before beginning to fade away, its face at last becoming a picture of resignation and finally resolution...

AFTER A FAIR BIT OF EFFORT, BRANDON SUCCEEDED IN PREVENTING ACCESS TO THE OLD SMUGGLER'S COVE. THE GUNPOWDER WAS QUITE DAMP... WHICH WAS PROBABLY WHY HE ENDED UP SLIGHTLY OVER ESTIMATING HOW MUCH TO APPLY TO THE SMALL TASK IN HAND.

UNFORTUNATELY THE EXPLOSION HAD AN EVEN WIDER IMPACT THAN INTENDED. SOME OF THE DEBRIS FLEW FOR QUITE A DISTANCE... OF ALL THE PLACES THAT IT CHOSE TO LAND, IT CHOSE THE SEAFARERS' CENTRE. THE MAJORITY OF THE SCHOOL PARTY HAD ONLY JUST LEFT, AFTER FINISHING LUNCH AND HAD BEEN ENJOYING AN ICE CREAM NEARBY. IT WAS ALL VERY EMBARRASSING INDEED.

164

FORTUNATELY IT WASN'T THAT DIFFICULT TO RESOLVE, OR REPAIR...

Excerpt From Linda Newbery's Diary (by Linda Newbery)

... so I'd have to carry on looking. I walked and walked until a blister on my heel made me stop on a grass verge to see if I had a plaster in my rucksack.

Just then, a coach coming from the Whitby direction braked suddenly and stopped quite near me. I saw from the driver's startled expression that he'd seen something in the road, and that made me wonder. Then he saw me, and must have thought I wanted a lift, because the door wheezed open. The coach was full of teenagers in school uniform. They all stared at me, so I stepped up inside and explained that I was looking for someone.

The driver said he'd need more to go on than that, so I tried, though I always have trouble with this. I mean, what *does* he look like, my man? I've never seen him clearly enough to know. So I said,

"Well – he's sort of greeny-browny, a bit woody, a bit barky, a bit leafy. You see him and then he's gone. He sort of – merges in."

Well, it turned out that the driver *had* seen someone just like that.

"That's why I slammed on the brakes!" he told me. *"Wandered out right in front of the coach, he did."*

One of the girls called out that she'd seen him as well; then the boy next to her, who'd been staring at me, said,

"I recognise you! You're a famous author, aren't you? I saw your photo in a book."

I blushed, because this doesn't happen very often. But then I heard the boy telling the others, *"It's Michelle Magorian! You know, who wrote that brilliant book 'Goodnight Mister Tom.'"* Next minute everyone was asking for my autograph. So I had to tell them that I'm not her, but yes, I am an author.

"How long have you been walking?" asked a man who must have been their teacher.

I told him how I'd lost my character, my man – how he kept wandering off, taking to the roads. Most people can't see him – in fact I can't, most of the time – but every now and then I come across one of those special people who can. And there were two of those here on this coach – the driver, and the girl at the front. Maybe more than two.

Several of them were listening by now.
"We're writing a book, too!" one of the boys told me. *"Our second, actually."*

This was impressive, so when they asked for a bit more about my lost character and what he's looking for, I tried to tell them, breaking my rule of never talking to anyone about a book until it's finished. I told them how he's been walking and walking the roads for hundreds of years to find the right person, and when he does, he stays with them.

By now I was sitting down on the steps, sharing a packet of crisps with the teacher. The driver seemed in no hurry, and had taken out his flask.

"Could we have your man in our story?" someone asked. *"I mean, just borrow him – you can have him back when we've finished."*

Well! I wasn't sure about that. He's not exactly *mine*; other people know him, too. But I can't have him meandering off into other people's stories – I have enough trouble keeping track of him as it is. Still, I wanted to give them something, because it's not every day you come across a group of teenagers who not only read books, but write them as well.

So instead I gave them a favourite quotation of mine, which seemed relevant. It's by Michael de Larrabeiti, an author some of them probably know. In this story, a Baron complains that he's never found happiness, and a wiser man answers like this:

"Know this, fool, you will never turn a bend in the road and find happiness waiting for you at the end of the journey as if it were a city ... happiness is the road itself, and you must walk it."

Isn't that great? And they seemed pleased with it. So we said goodbye and good luck, and I got off the coach and carried on walking, wondering what sort of story they would write.

SINCE THEIR VISITS TO THE YORKSHIRE MINING MUSEUM, SCARBOROUGH AND WHITBY THE 'IRON PYRATES,' THE ICT TEAM, PRIMARY STUDENTS AND TEACHERS FROM THE HILL, CARRFIELD, GOOSEACRE AND HIGHGATE AND LOADS OF OTHER STUDENTS AND STAFF, HAD SPENT SUBSTANTIAL HOURS TRYING TO COMPLETE THEIR BOOK.

THE FINAL TOUCHES TO EDITING WERE BEING COMPLETED AS MRS DAVIS PROUDLY ENTERED TO VIEW THE WORK AND TALK TO THE STUDENTS.

I'VE HEARD SO MUCH ABOUT THIS... BUT I'VE NEVER ACTUALLY SEEN ANY OF IT.

NINE PIECES OF GOLD
(by Ian McMillan)

First Piece:

They used to till the fields
Horses pulled the plough
Corn grew in Barnsley accents
And thi fatha milked a cow
Fool's Gold
Fool's Gold

Second Piece:

They used to harvest crops
They used to grind the corn
Fed their bairns turnip tops
'Mines nesh: how's yourn ?'
Fool's Gold
Fool's Gold

Third Piece

Then they discovered coal
Black gold under the soil
Then the fields were full of holes
And the families dug the coyle
Fool's Gold
Fool's Gold

Fourth Piece

And the owners made the dosh
And they got filthy rich
Dressed nice and talked quite posh
While the poor drank from a ditch
Fool's Gold
Fool's Gold

Fifth piece

And for years the pits were there
And the coal was dug and burned
And the smoke hung in the air
And the lessons could be learned
Fool's Gold
Fool's Gold

Sixth Piece

But now the pits are gone
Miners struck and fought and lost
But the memories will live on
And the landscape counts the cost
Fool's Gold
Fool's Gold

Seventh Piece

Write a poem, sing a song
Tell a story, write a book
Make it short or make it long
This is Yorkshire: have a look
Real Gold
Real Gold

Eighth Piece

The past is in its place
The past has been and gone
The future's in my face
This place will carry on
True Gold
True Gold

Ninth Piece

The memories that we hold
The stories we pass on
Are pure and shining gold
That will keep shining when we're gone...
Pure Gold
Pure Gold

THE POEM 'NINE PIECES OF GOLD' WAS LATER ADAPTED AND BECAME A SONG TO BE PERFORMED BY THE COLLEGE'S BTEC DRAMA GROUP AND THE IAN McMILLAN ORCHESTRA. - 'THESE WILL BE MEMORIES THAT WE HOLD...'

MRS TOWNEND HAD PHOTOGRAPHED EVERYTHING TO REPRESENT - 'THE STORIES WE PASS ON...'

THE ICT TEAM SET TO WORK ENSURING THE GRAPHIC IMAGES WERE - 'PURE AND SHINING GOLD, THAT WILL KEEP SHINING WHEN WE'VE GONE...' AND SO YOU HAVE NOW VIRTUALLY READ OUR STORY FROM COVER TO COVER...

179

Afterword

'Fool's Gold' is the second book published by the Dearne High: A Specialist Humanities College. The first, 'Out of the Shadows: An Anthology of Fantasy stories,' was sold across the internet, in house and at regional Waterstones and W H Smiths' stores from October 2008 onwards. It attracted a lot of interest from people involved in the book trade. As a result, no less than fourteen highly reputable writers, graphic artists and photographers have contributed towards the production of 'Fool's Gold' since the project began in January 2009.

'Fool's Gold' is a far more ambitious and wider reaching book than our first. It is a complex book about books, containing adventures equally real and fictional, with layers of detail both simple and subtle. Written by students, for students, it is also a book that should appeal to all ages.

The project to produce the book was a once in a life time experience. It contained amusing and sometimes very challenging moments that came about because a multitude of people were contributing sections at different times with only my plot synopsis and chapter briefs to work from. Patience was a virtue that we all had to utilise fully. I was therefore very grateful for the compassion shown, particularly by some bestselling writers who tolerated a few small compromises along the way and helped us make useful amendments and improvements.

We were also very appreciative to Darren Shan for his congratulatory signed messages to authors of our first book – 'Out of the Shadows.' His support really helped inspire our students to put in the effort to produce an even better book than the first. We were therefore delighted that Darren granted us permission to include his photograph with our students, within the closing stages of our book. Ours is after all, a truly unique story that is all about our children working with many of the best children's authors around at the beginning of the 21st century.

(Pictured from left to right – Kayleigh Webster, Brandon Noble, Scott Boardman, Lauren Eggison, Kimberely Hempshall Alicia Foster and Darren Shan)

It remains to say a special thanks to Mark Denton, Jo Curley and Joe Cornish for their support in providing photographs and inspiring our students and staff. I thought it more than appropriate, as Mark, Jo and Joe's photos were 'altered' to blend in with the graphic format of the text, to reprint them in their original format. All three are 'magicians of light' and their support, along with that from a plethora of people was a privilege that I will cherish for many years to come.

Peter Shaw
September 2009

Photographs Of Scarborough by Mark Denton

('North Bay Dusk, Scarborough' – Mark Denton)

('Reflections, Scarborough South Bay' – Mark Denton)

('Roof top Snow – Scarborough' – Mark Denton)

('Funfair – Scarborough Harbour' – Mark Denton)

A Photograph Of Whitby by Jo Curley

('Whitby Panorama' – Jo Curley)

Photographs Of Whitby by Joe Cornish

'Whitby, St Marys' – Joe Cornish

'Whitby, Blue Steps' – Joe Cornish

'Whitby Abbey, Frost' – Joe Cornish

'Whitby Abbey' – Joe Cornish

'Whitby Abbey, Sunset' – Joe Cornish